STUDENT WORKBOOK

for
Personal Financial Literacy

CONTENTS

PREFACE

The *Student Workbook* offers practice exercises that help you learn to excel in personal finance. For each chapter of the text, the workbook includes the following sections:

- **Vocabulary Check**—questions ask you to fill in the blanks to help you review vocabulary terms from the chapter.

- **Check Your Knowledge**—includes ten multiple choice questions to test your knowledge of concepts covered in the chapter.

- **Math Check Up**—has five word problems to help you practice math skills related to personal finance topics discussed in the chapter.

- **Open Response**—consists of two short essay questions, each describing an everyday financial situation for you to analyze. It also includes scoring guides to make sure you answer each part of the questions completely.

- **Activities**—include two to four personal finance activities to help you apply concepts from the chapter to your own finances. Check the Companion Website (PearsonSchool.com/PersonalFinance) for more activities that include Excel spreadsheets and Word documents.

Editor in Chief: Donna Battista
Acquisitions Editor: Katie Rowland
Editorial Project Manager: Emily Biberger
Managing Editor: Jeff Holcomb
Associate Production Project Manager: Alison Eusden
Senior Manufacturing Buyer: Carol Melville
Cover Designer: Stephanie Lindsey
Full-Service Project Management and Composition: Gillian Hall

10 9 8 7 6 5 4 3 2 1

PearsonSchool.com/Advanced

ISBN 10: 0-13-216756-5
ISBN 13: 978-0-13-216756-7

CHAPTER 1

Overview of Personal Finance
VOCABULARY CHECK

| bankruptcy |
| liquid asset |
| opportunity cost |
| personal finance |
| personal financial planning |

1. Samantha wants to learn more about financial issues that can affect her life. She is learning about _____.

2. The process of _____ will help George plan his financial future.

3. Leon used money from his savings account for a down payment on an ATV. Money in his savings account is an example of a _____.

4. _____ is a legal process filed when one is unable to pay bills.

5. Allison wanted to spend the evening at the movies with friends instead of filling her car's gas tank. With this decision she incurred an _____.

CHAPTER 1

Overview of Personal Finance

CHECK YOUR KNOWLEDGE

Multiple Choice Questions *Circle the correct answer for each of the following.*

1. The process of planning every aspect of your personal finances is known as _____.
   a. budgeting
   b. money management
   c. personal financial planning
   d. financial security administration

2. Liquid assets are those possessions that can be readily and easily converted to _____.
   a. cash
   b. liquid
   c. stocks
   d. bonds

3. All of the following are important in choosing a career except _____.
   a. compensation
   b. benefit packages
   c. interests
   d. gender

4. Your gross pay will be reduced by _____.
   a. taxes
   b. car payments
   c. house payments
   d. clothing

5. In general, the _____ education and training you get, the _____ you will earn in your lifetime.
   a. more, less
   b. less, less
   c. less, more
   d. more, more

6. Good financial planning can help you achieve all of the following goals except _____.
   a. winning the lottery
   b. buying a car
   c. learning a new skill
   d. funding your retirement

7. The median home price in the United States for 2010 was _____.
   a. about $222,000
   b. more than $500,000
   c. about $150,000
   d. less than $125,000

8. People should begin planning for retirement at age _____.
   a. 50
   b. 40
   c. 30
   d. 20

9. Which of the following goals is not a financial goal?
   a. give $100,000 to charity
   b. earn a college degree
   c. retire with $1,000,000 in assets
   d. all of the above are financial goals

10. Most people in the United States save _____ percent of their income.
   a. 10
   b. 20
   c. 0
   d. 15

CHAPTER 1

Overview of Personal Finance
MATH CHECK UP

Instructions: *In the space provided, answer each of the following math problems. Be sure to show your work in the space provided.*

1. If you save $15 a week for the next two years instead of buying music, how much money would you accumulate ignoring interest?

2. What is the opportunity cost of buying a $.75 soda every school day for three years instead of drinking water? Assume you are in school for 36 weeks a year and that water is free.

3. Assume you want to accumulate $4,000 to begin investing at the end of three years. How much money would you need to save every week to accomplish that goal?

4. What is the opportunity cost of going to the arcade on Saturday night assuming you could make $8 an hour for four hours of work and you also spend about $25 each time you go to the arcade?

5. Your uncle has agreed to sell you his car for $3,000. You will put $2,000 down and pay him the rest over the next 40 weeks. How much will your weekly payment be?

CHAPTER 1

Overview of Personal Finance

OPEN RESPONSE #1: Making a Personal Financial Plan

Please answer all parts of the question in the space provided.

Prompt: Antonio has decided to begin a lawn care business. He wants to begin saving for a car and have money after high school graduation. He knows that he will need to invest money to begin his business but at the same time he has already checked into what others are charging for lawn care. Antonio does not know where to begin to make his financial goals a reality.

1. Explain to Antonio why he needs to make a personal financial plan.

2. What information does Antonio need to include in his financial plan?

Scoring Guide

4 Student gives correct answers for parts 1 and 2. All explanations are clear and complete. There is evidence of clear understanding of the concept.

3 Student gives correct answers for parts 1 and 2. Explanations are correct, but possibly unclear. There is less evidence of clear understanding.

2 Student answers 1 (1 or 2) part of the questions completely correct. There is some evidence of understanding.

1 Student gives only parts of correct answers. There is little evidence of understanding.

0 Response is totally incorrect or irrelevant (does not add any new information to the question).

_____

_____

_____

_____

_____

_____

_____

_____

_____

_____

_____

_____

CHAPTER 1

Overview of Personal Finance

OPEN RESPONSE #2: Making Financial Decisions

Please answer all parts of the question in the space provided.

Prompt: Colton earns $35 per lawn he mows. In one day he mows four lawns and he works five days a week for 20 weeks a year. His expenses for his lawn care business are $12 for gas in his mower per day; $75 for gas in his truck every two weeks; and $8 for gas in the trimmer and blower every week.

Colton wants to buy a new truck this fall. The truck is a used truck that his father's friend is selling for $5,200. One of Colton's friends wants to buy his truck for $1,500. Colton's buddies are planning a fishing trip during the lawn season that will cost Colton $250 for his expenses to go along. However, he will also have to get someone to mow his lawns and take care of his customers. Colton believes he can hire Jim for $120 per day and let Jim use his equipment.

1. What advice can you give Colton to help him with the financial decisions he needs to make?

2. How do opportunity costs factor into his decision to go on the fishing trip? What if he decides to buy the new truck?

Scoring Guide

4 Student gives correct answers for parts 1 and 2. All explanations are clear and complete. There is evidence of clear understanding of the concept.

3 Student gives correct answers for parts 1 and 2. Explanations are correct, but possibly unclear. There is less evidence of clear understanding.

2 Student answers 1 (1 or 2) part of the questions completely correct. There is some evidence of understanding.

1 Student gives only parts of correct answers. There is little evidence of understanding.

0 Response is totally incorrect or irrelevant (does not add any new information to the question).

_____

_____

_____

_____

_____

_____

_____

CHAPTER 1

Overview of Personal Finance

ACTIVITY #1: Planning for an Event

Instructions:

1. Develop a plan for an event you wish to attend. This might be a school dance, a training camp for a school sport, dance team, or cheerleading. It could be a student organization you participate in that is attending a conference. You might also want to plan for a vacation during spring break.

2. Write down all the steps you will need to complete to be prepared for the event. These steps might include getting your finances in place and determining what clothing and food to take. Do you need to take a sleeping bag, pillows, or your own bed linens? This first step needs to be a brainstorming activity where you think about all that the event involves.

3. Once you have completed your brainstorming, you will need to prioritize your list. What do you need to complete first? What is the last step before the event that needs to be completed?

4. Have a fellow classmate look over your list to see that all the steps needed for a successful event are complete.

Planning for an Event

Brainstorm List	Prioritized List

SCANS Foundation Skills: Basic and Thinking
SCANS Workplace Skills: Resources, Information, and Systems

CHAPTER 1

Overview of Personal Finance

ACTIVITY #2: Financial Decision Making

Instructions:

1. Write down three purchases (buying soft drinks for a week, going to a movie with friends, purchasing a new iPod, and so on) that you would like to make in the next month. Assume you will forego income of $10 per hour for any purchase that involves time.

2. Write down any income you have coming in over the next month. This could be from your job, allowance, or birthday/holiday money.

3. Determine the opportunity cost for each of the items you wish to purchase. Which purchase would be the best decision for now?

Purchase	Cost to You	Hours of Work Missed	Opportunity Cost	Total Cost
1.				
2.				
3.				
Best Choice:				

CHAPTER 2

The Financial Plan

VOCABULARY CHECK

1. Tora wants to have financial success, so she developed a

   _____.

2. Clayton planned his spending and saving for the next three months by _____ his money.

3. Rafael's dad added up his assets and subtracted his liabilities to determine his _____.

4. Lorenzo listed his motorcycle as an _____ on his bank loan.

5. Lorenzo listed the remaining $1,500 he owes on his motorcycle as a _____.

6. Lorenzo's motorcycle is worth $5,000. He has $3,500 in _____ in the motorcycle.

7. Sasha makes $1,120 per month at her job and receives $50 per month in allowance. The $1,170 per month is listed as _____ on her financial plan.

8. Tamara needed $150 by next week to pay for a new dance team warm-up suit. She looked at her _____ to determine her ability to pay for the warm-up suit by the due date.

9. Good _____ would help Tamara be prepared for extracurricular activities expenses.

10. Javier received a credit card application in the mail. His parents talked with Javier about good _____ before he applied for credit.

11. Javier noticed that the credit card company charged 18 percent _____ each month.

12. Javier's parents went over the _____ of the credit card with him so that he would fully understand when his payment would be due if he used the card.

13. Geoff bought the least insurance coverage on his car. He is taking a _____ that if his car is damaged the insurance will cover all costs to get it repaired.

14. Rachel had little savings, so she knew she would have to _____ the purchase of her car.

15. _____ is not a very liquid investment because it is not always easy or possible to quickly sell buildings and land.

asset
budgeting
credit management
equity
finance
income
interest
liability
liquidity
money management
net worth
payment terms
personal financial plan
real estate
risk

CHAPTER 2

The Financial Plan

CHECK YOUR KNOWLEDGE

Multiple Choice Questions *Circle the correct answer for each of the following.*

1. Which of the following is not a component of a financial plan?
   a. a plan to manage risk
   b. a plan to pay utility bills
   c. a plan for investing
   d. a plan for retirement

2. Your net worth is the difference between your _____.
   a. assets and liabilities
   b. payments and income
   c. cash inflows and outflows
   d. liquid assets and long-term assets

3. Which of the following is not a source of income?
   a. wages
   b. salary
   c. allowance
   d. car payment

4. A person's income may depend on all of the following except _____.
   a. career choice
   b. height
   c. education
   d. training

5. Consumers tend to spend the most money on which category of goods?
   a. food
   b. entertainment
   c. housing
   d. clothing

6. Assume you intend to borrow $5,000. Which of the following financing terms is the best deal?
   a. 5 percent for 4 years
   b. 9 percent for 5 years
   c. 8 percent for 3 years
   d. 9.5 percent for 6 years

7. Which of the following is a key component of risk management?
   a. insurance
   b. investments
   c. cash
   d. jewelry

8. In general, the higher the risk of a particular investment the higher the potential
_____.
   a. debt
   b. return
   c. liquidity
   d. record keeping

9. The most common investments include _____.
   a. stocks and bonds
   b. stamp collections
   c. rare automobiles
   d. oil paintings

10. Good record keeping is important for _____.
   a. tax purposes
   b. calculating net worth
   c. estate planning
   d. young children

CHAPTER 2

The Financial Plan
MATH CHECK UP

Instructions: *In the space provided, answer each of the following math problems. Be sure to show your work in the space provided.*

1. Assume you have a car worth $3,200 and investments worth another $7,500. If you owe $1,300 on credit cards and that is your only debt, how much is your net worth?

2. How much does Jill have in liquid assets if her car is worth $4,500 and she has $1,110 in a savings account and $532 in her checking account?

3. If you buy a car for $7,500 and put $2,200 down, how much equity will you have in the car?

4. Assume you purchased a car for $2,300 and sold it one week later for $3,100. How much did your net worth change, if at all?

5. You have decided to save 20 percent of your income for the next two years. Assuming you bring home $125 a week, how much will you save over that time?

CHAPTER 2

The Financial Plan

OPEN RESPONSE #1: Planning for Your Financial Future

Please answer all parts of the question in the space provided.

Prompt: Meghan is beginning to think about her future and what it will cost to live the lifestyle she would like to enjoy. She has come to you for advice on how to make money and have money in the future to live comfortably.

1. Explain to Meghan how to secure her financial future.

2. What recommendations would you make to Meghan as she begins planning for her financial future? Give specific examples of what she might do to secure her future financially.

Scoring Guide

4 Student gives correct answers for parts 1 and 2. All explanations are clear and complete. There is evidence of clear understanding of the concept.

3 Student gives correct answers for parts 1 and 2. Explanations are correct, but possibly unclear. There is less evidence of clear understanding.

2 Student answers 1 (1 or 2) part of the questions completely correct. There is some evidence of understanding.

1 Student gives only parts of correct answers. There is little evidence of understanding.

0 Response is totally incorrect or irrelevant (does not add any new information to the question).

_____

_____

_____

_____

_____

_____

_____

_____

_____

_____

_____

SCANS Foundation Skills: Basic and Thinking
SCANS Workplace Skills: Resources, Interpersonal, Information, and Systems

CHAPTER 2

The Financial Plan

OPEN RESPONSE #2: Wants versus Needs

Please answer all parts of the question in the space provided.

Prompt: Morgan's parents have decided that it will be up to him to pay for all his "wants" (movie tickets, extra gas for the car, updated cell phone, shoes for skateboarding, and so on), but they explain that they will cover all his "needs" (food, housing, necessary clothing, and so on). Morgan was not prepared to think about his finances and paying for all the extras.

1. What advice can you give Morgan so that he will have the money to pay for his "wants"?

2. How will this unexpected spending impact his financial plan? What advice can you give him about his financial plan?

Scoring Guide

4 Student gives correct answers for parts 1 and 2. All explanations are clear and complete. There is evidence of clear understanding of the concept.

3 Student gives correct answers for parts 1 and 2. Explanations are correct, but possibly unclear. There is less evidence of clear understanding.

2 Student answers 1 (1 or 2) part of the questions completely correct. There is some evidence of understanding.

1 Student gives only parts of correct answers. There is little evidence of understanding.

0 Response is totally incorrect or irrelevant (does not add any new information to the question).

_____

_____

_____

_____

_____

_____

_____

_____

_____

_____

_____

_____

SCANS Foundation Skills: Basic and Thinking
SCANS Workplace Skills: Resources, Interpersonal, Information, and Systems

CHAPTER 2

The Financial Plan

ACTIVITY #1: Weekly Spending

Last Week		This Week	
Items	Total	Items	Total

Instructions:

1. In the chart above, identify purchases you made last week. You may have had more than you have room to list here, so you might need to use extra paper. You may not have spent any or very little last week.

2. Think about what you have spent so far this week. In the chart above, list these purchases. Again, if you have more purchases than there is space, use extra paper. It is not a problem if you do not fill all the boxes.

3. Look over both lists.
    a. Do you notice differences?
    b. Did you have anything special (school function, vacation, holiday, birthday—friend or family, or such) during the two weeks you are reviewing?
    c. Can you see a trend in your expenses?

4. Write a narrative explaining your spending during these two weeks. Use your answers to step 3 to help you describe what is happening to your money. Is there somewhere you could cut down on spending? Explain. Could you save more? How?

SCANS Foundation Skills: Basic, Thinking, and Personal Qualities
SCANS Workplace Skills: Resources and Information

CHAPTER 2

The Financial Plan

ACTIVITY #2: Plan for Communication

Instructions:

1. Brainstorm a list of who you could talk with about your financial plans.

2. Make a list of how you can communicate your financial plan.

3. Prepare a chart, either using spreadsheet software or paper/pencil, that shows how and to whom you can communicate your financial plans.

4. In the space provided below, explain the importance of communicating your financial plan.

_____

_____

_____

_____

_____

_____

_____

_____

_____

_____

_____

_____

_____

_____

_____

_____

_____

_____

_____

_____

SCANS Foundation Skills: Basic, Thinking, and Personal Qualities
SCANS Workplace Skills: Resources, Information, Systems, and Technology

CHAPTER 3

Financial Decision Making
VOCABULARY CHECK

1. Jayna wants to purchase a new iPod this month. This type of goal would be a _____.

2. Cam is planning on going to the movie with friends this Saturday. This would be considered a(n) _____ because he would be spending money.

3. J.P. hopes to become an NFL player after college. He graduates high school this year so this type of goal is a(n) _____.

4. Charlotte found that her cell-phone bill was a _____ expense. She might make more calls one month than the next.

5. Zoe received $25 for her birthday. This would be considered a(n) _____ in her financial plan.

6. Typical _____ for teens include clothing, entertainment, or gasoline. The money Josef receives from working is considered _____.

7. The house that Tabitha plans to purchase when she has worked for 10 years is going to be great. This goal is one of her _____.

8. Derrick's car payment is considered a _____.

9. Shirley can _____ the amount of income she will receive from her scholarship for next fall.

10. Jean wanted to buy a sports car after high school until she found out how much the insurance coverage would be. Her insurance company charges higher rates for sports cars because they are higher _____.

---

cash inflow

cash outflow

expense

fixed expense

forecast

income

long-term goal

intermediate-term goal

risk

short-term goal

variable expense

CHAPTER 3

Financial Decision Making
CHECK YOUR KNOWLEDGE

Multiple Choice Questions *Circle the correct answer for each of the following.*

1. Cash inflows include all of the following except _____.
   a. rent paid
   b. salary
   c. allowance
   d. dividends received

2. Long-term goals take at least _____ year(s) to complete.
   a. 10
   b. 30
   c. 5
   d. 20

3. Cash outflows include all of the following except _____.
   a. rent paid
   b. salary
   c. utilities
   d. car payments

4. Short-term goals will be accomplished in the next _____.
   a. year
   b. 5 years
   c. 10 years
   d. 6 months

5. It is essential that you establish goals that are _____.
   a. unrealistic
   b. realistic
   c. short-term instead of long-term
   d. unachievable

6. Which of the following is not an expense?
   a. rent
   b. savings
   c. lunch expenditures
   d. money spent on gas

7. Risk is defined as _____.
   a. a physical challenge
   b. skydiving
   c. the likelihood of loss
   d. choosing a dangerous profession

8. All financial goals should be periodically evaluated and _____ if necessary.
   a. revised
   b. abandoned
   c. thrown away
   d. eliminated

9. Financial decision making involves all of the following except _____.
   a. establishing goals
   b. evaluating your current financial position
   c. revising plans as necessary
   d. motivating your friends to support you

10. Sabrena decided she wants to save $300,000 by the time she turns 25. She currently makes $100 a week and will turn age 18 next month. This is an example of a(n) _____ goal.
   a. realistic
   b. unrealistic
   c. achievable
   d. short-term

CHAPTER 3

Financial Decision Making
MATH CHECK UP

Instructions: *In the space provided, answer each of the following math problems. Be sure to show your work in the space provided.*

1. If Jared makes $200 a week working on cars but he spends $25 a week on uniforms, how much money will he accumulate in one year if he saves all his employment income?

2. Steven switched phone carriers to one that charges $40 a month for unlimited calls. Assuming he has been spending $75 a month for phone service, how much will he save in 18 months?

3. Drake's monthly outlays include a $70 phone bill and a $120 car payment. Assuming he makes $400 a month, how much does he have to spend after paying his bills?

4. Brianne wants to save an additional $2,000 in the next 16 months. Assuming she brings home $8 an hour, how many extra hours a month will she need to work to achieve this goal?

5. If you make $450 a month but 15 percent is held out of each paycheck for social security and taxes, how much do you bring home?

CHAPTER 3

Financial Decision Making
OPEN RESPONSE #1: Making Choices

Please answer all parts of the question in the space provided.

Prompt: Creighton wants to purchase a sound system to install in his bedroom. He has most of the money saved to purchase the system. However, Creighton's parents want him to save the money for college next year. They are worried about expenses that might not be covered by his scholarship.

Creighton is sure that his parents are worried about nothing. What could happen? Besides he has a job and can just make more money. Creighton comes to you asking for support in his decision to purchase the sound system. He is sure that you will understand and help him with his argument with his parents on spending the money now.

1. What questions would you advise Creighton to ask himself about this purchase?

2. What recommendation(s) would you make to Creighton about purchasing the sound system? Give examples he might use to defend his choice to purchase the sound system or examples that help him to understand his parents' point of view.

Scoring Guide

4 Student gives correct answers for parts 1 and 2. All explanations are clear and complete. There is evidence of clear understanding of the concept.

3 Student gives correct answers for parts 1 and 2. Explanations are correct, but possibly unclear. There is less evidence of clear understanding.

2 Student answers 1 (1 or 2) part of the questions completely correct. There is some evidence of understanding.

1 Student gives only parts of correct answers. There is little evidence of understanding.

0 Response is totally incorrect or irrelevant (does not add any new information to the question).

SCANS Foundation Skills: Basic and Thinking
SCANS Workplace Skills: Resources, Interpersonal, Information, and Systems

CHAPTER 3

Financial Decision Making

OPEN RESPONSE #2: Establishing Financial Goals

Please answer all parts of the question in the space provided.

Prompt: Ariadne has begun to think about her financial future. In particular, she wants to attend beauty school after high school graduation. One day she would like to own a day spa featuring the best in hair and personal care.

1. What advice can you give Ariadne about establishing her financial goals?

2. Explain to Ariadne how setting goals affects her financial plan. Give examples of what might happen if goals are or are not set.

Scoring Guide

4 Student gives correct answers for parts 1 and 2. All explanations are clear and complete. There is evidence of clear understanding of the concept.

3 Student gives correct answers for parts 1 and 2. Explanations are correct, but possibly unclear. There is less evidence of clear understanding.

2 Student answers 1 (1 or 2) part of the questions completely correct. There is some evidence of understanding.

1 Student gives only parts of correct answers. There is little evidence of understanding.

0 Response is totally incorrect or irrelevant (does not add any new information to the question).

_____

_____

_____

_____

_____

_____

_____

_____

_____

_____

_____

_____

SCANS Foundation Skills: Basic and Thinking
SCANS Workplace Skills: Resources, Interpersonal, Information, and Systems

CHAPTER 3

Financial Decision Making

ACTIVITY #1: Personal Financial Goals

Financial Goal	Dollar Amount to Accomplish	Priority (low, medium, or high)
Short-Term Goals		
1.		
2.		
3.		
Middle-Term Goals		
1.		
2.		
3.		
Long-Term Goals		
1.		
2.		
3.		

Instructions:

1. Use the chart to fill in your short-, middle-, and long-term goals. You may have less than three or more than three. If you have more than three, you might want to look at just the top three picks for each.

2. Next, you will want to prioritize your goals. In other words, look at each item under each goal. Which would you like to accomplish first (high)? Which has your least concern (low)?

3. Looking at your goals (short, middle, and long), determine what you need to do to accomplish these goals. Is additional education or training needed? Do you need to save more money? Work more hours? Write a letter to yourself describing your goals and what you need to do to accomplish your most important goals.

SCANS Foundation Skills: Basic, Thinking, and Personal
SCANS Workplace Skills: Resources, Information, and Systems

CHAPTER 3

Financial Decision Making

ACTIVITY #2: Identify and Evaluate Options for Accomplishing Your Goals

Goal: _____

Option 1:	Pros	Cons
Option 2:	Pros	Cons
Option 3:	Pros	Cons

Instructions:

In Activity #1 you determined your short-, middle-, and long-term goals. Now, consider your options for accomplishing your long-term goal.

1. In the form above, write down your high priority long-term goal.

2. Next, think about and list three options you have to accomplish this goal.

3. Now, write the pros and cons of each option you have listed. What are the benefits and drawbacks of each option?

4. Write an opinion paper that discusses each option and which option has the lowest cost but the highest benefit.

CHAPTER 3

Financial Decision Making

ACTIVITY #3: Steps of Financial Decision Making

Instructions:

Develop a chart that helps you to remember the steps of financial decision making. Use your creativity to develop your design. You might consider making a poster that shows each step. You might want to make a computer presentation that shows the steps.

1. Be sure that your chart has an explanation for each step.

2. Include an example to help demonstrate what you would do at each step.

3. Use the information throughout this chapter to help you put the steps in order. You might also want to search the Internet to help you describe each step.

CHAPTER 4

Budgets and Balance Sheets:
Your Personal Financial Statements

VOCABULARY CHECK

bond
budget
current liability
forecast error
household asset
investment
liability
liquid asset
long-term liability
market value
mutual fund
net worth
personal balance sheet
real estate
stock

1. Samantha decided to sell her ATV so she could have extra cash for books when she began vocational school after graduation. She bought the ATV for $2,300 but sold it for $1,200. This lower price is the _____ of the ATV.

2. XYZ Company has decided to raise money by issuing debt in $1,000 increments that are known as _____.

3. Terris needs to forecast his future cash inflow and outflow. To help him do this he must create a _____ that will help with his financial planning.

4. Meghan's grandfather left a portion of his farm to her in his will. Upon his death, Meghan will own _____ and can count this as an asset.

5. Georgia takes a look at her budget. She sees a difference in what she forecast would happen and what is really happening. This difference is known as _____.

6. Antwone needs to keep track of how much money he is worth. One tool that he could use to help make this decision is a _____.

7. Jonathan's car was having brake problems. He needed cash fast to help pay for repairs. He had set aside some money in _____ that should be enough to cover the repairs.

8. David's parents invested in a _____ as part of their Section 529 College Savings Plan for his higher education.

9. Terris wanted to get a loan but needed to lists his assets. He already knew the value of his violin but needed to include his car, furniture, entertainment system, and other _____.

10. Jonathan's credit card debt is a _____ , while his student loan for school is a _____.

11. Terris purchased a violin that would grow in value over time. Terris decided this would be a good _____ in his future as a professional musician.

12. When Joley's dad decided to start a business, he sold _____ to investors as part ownership in the business.

13. Jonathan owes $2,000 on his credit card. This is listed as a _____ on his balance sheet.

14. When Terris calculates his assets and subtracts his liabilities, the difference is his _____.

CHAPTER 4

Budgets and Balance Sheets:
Your Personal Financial Statements

CHECK YOUR KNOWLEDGE

Asset or Liability? You be the judge. In the blank beside each word place an **A** if it is an asset or an **L** if it is a liability. Remember, assets are things you own or possess and liabilities are debts that you owe.

_____ Car   _____ Credit card bill

_____ Car note   _____ Xbox

_____ Dirt bike   _____ Clothing

_____ IBM stock   _____ Cash

_____ Savings account   _____ $20 you owe a friend

_____ Mutual fund   _____ Past due amount for lunch

_____ A loan from your parents   _____ Guitar

Multiple Choice Questions *Circle the correct answer for each of the following.*

1. Which of the following is not a tool for monitoring your finances?
  a. personal balance sheet
  b. budget
  c. liability
  d. cash flow statement

2. One way to increase savings is to _____ cash inflows.
  a. increase
  b. decrease
  c. spend
  d. monitor

3. A scholarship would be an example of a cash _____.
  a. outflow
  b. inflow
  c. decrease
  d. statement

4. Which of the following is not an asset?
  a. car
  b. stock
  c. credit card bill
  d. jewelry

5. Shares of ownership in a company are represented by _____.
  a. bonds
  b. stocks
  c. assets
  d. liabilities

33

6. Your net worth is calculated by summing up the value of your _____ and subtracting your liabilities.
   a. stocks
   b. cars
   c. assets
   d. debts

7. Which of the following is more likely to be a long-term liability?
   a. house payment
   b. credit card bill
   c. electric bill
   d. water bill

8. If you buy land that increases in value your _____ will increase as long as your debt remains the same or declines.
   a. net worth
   b. liabilities
   c. budget
   d. cash flows

9. If your total debt is $4,500 and the value of your assets is $9,100 then your debt-to-asset ratio is equal to _____.
   a. 2.02 percent
   b. 49.40 percent
   c. 57.05 percent
   d. 50.60 percent

10. Which of the following is a type of college savings plan created by the government to encourage people to save for their children's and grandchildren's education?
    a. bond savings alternatives
    b. stock plans
    c. Section 529 plans
    d. IRS college funds

CHAPTER 4

Budgets and Balance Sheets:
Your Personal Financial Statements

MATH CHECK UP

Instructions: *In the space provided, answer each of the following math problems. Be sure to show your work in the space provided.*

1. Tammy owns a laptop computer she paid $1,200 for about two years ago. Today, she thinks she could sell it for about $700. She also has a car worth $2,900 on which she still owes $800 and that will be paid off next year. How much is her net worth?

2. Valerie's monthly income is $450 and her monthly outflows are $425. How much money could Valerie save in the next eight months without changing her income or spending patterns?

3. Jamal wants to save at least 8 percent of his income every month for a year. Assume he gets a $100 allowance every month from his grandfather and he makes an average of $320 a month working part time after school. How much will he save in one year?

4. Lakita's dad was teaching her about the stock market. He has 100 shares of Company A stock valued at $45 a share and 250 shares of Company B stock valued at $22 a share. How much is his stock worth?

5. Jill estimated she would spend $50 a month on clothing. However, at the end of the year she discovered she actually spent $711 on clothing that year. What was her forecast error for that budget item?

CHAPTER 4

Budgets and Balance Sheets:
Your Personal Financial Statements

OPEN RESPONSE #1: Planning a Budget

Please answer all parts of the question in the space provided.

Prompt: Samantha wants to move into an apartment when she begins school in the fall. Right now she has a job where she makes $250 a week working 20 hours and will be able to keep this job once she begins school. Her parents have decided to put $500 a month in for extras that she might need once she begins school. Although Samantha is very excited about moving into an apartment, she wants your advice on where to begin preparing for her move. She wants to put together a budget but has no idea where to begin.

1. Explain to Samantha how to set up her budget.

2. Once Samantha has a budget, what should she consider when determining if moving out when she is beginning school is a good idea or not. Give specific reasons why this might be a good or bad idea.

Scoring Guide

4 Student gives correct answers for parts 1 and 2. All explanations are clear and complete. There is evidence of clear understanding of the concept.

3 Student gives correct answers for parts 1 and 2. Explanations are correct, but possibly unclear. There is less evidence of clear understanding.

2 Student answers 1 (1 or 2) part of the questions completely correct. There is some evidence of understanding.

1 Student gives only parts of correct answers. There is little evidence of understanding.

0 Response is totally incorrect or irrelevant (does not add any new information to the question).

_____

_____

_____

_____

_____

_____

_____

_____

_____

CHAPTER 4

Budgets and Balance Sheets:
Your Personal Financial Statements

OPEN RESPONSE #2: Cash Inflow and Cash Outflow

Please answer all parts of the question in the space provided.

Prompt: Below is Peter's weekly and monthly budget:

Peter's Budget

Cash Inflows	Typical Week	Typical Monthly Total
Disposable Income (after tax)	$125	$550
Allowance (from parents)	$50	$220
Total Cash Inflows	$175	$770
Cash Outflows		
Recreation	$60	$250
Gas (for parents' car)	$40	$180
Clothing	$10	$50
Cell Phone (with text messaging)	$12	$50
Other	$20	$100
Total Cash Outflows	$142	$630
Net Cash Flows	+ $33	+ $140

1. Peter wants to buy a used car. His father has agreed to put in half the cost of the car up to $2,500. What advice can you give Peter to help him save for the car he wants?

2. Once Peter purchases his car, how will this affect his cash outflow? What will he need to do to adjust his budget after the purchase of his car?

Scoring Guide

4 Student gives correct answers for parts 1 and 2. All explanations are clear and complete. There is evidence of clear understanding of the concept.

3 Student gives correct answers for parts 1 and 2. Explanations are correct, but possibly unclear. There is less evidence of clear understanding.

2 Student answers 1 (1 or 2) part of the questions completely correct. There is some evidence of understanding.

1 Student gives only parts of correct answers. There is little evidence of understanding.

0 Response is totally incorrect or irrelevant (does not add any new information to the question).

CHAPTER 4

Budgets and Balance Sheets:
Your Personal Financial Statements

Activity #1: Personal Cash Flow Statement

Personal Cash Flow Statement

Cash Inflows	Actual Amounts Last Week	Expected Amounts This Week
Disposable Income from Job (after tax)		
Allowance		
Special Event Monies (birthday money, graduation money, etc.)		
Other		
Total Cash Inflows		

Cash Outflows	Actual Amounts Last Week	Expected Amounts This Week
Car Payment		
Car Expenses (insurance, maintenance, and gas)		
Cell Phone		
Food (eating out and at home)		
Clothing		
Entertainment (movies, dates, etc.)		
Extra (makeup, hair products, etc.)		
Other		
Total Cash Outflows		
Net Cash Flow		

Instructions:

1. Determine your cash inflow for last week. This could be from a job you have, from an allowance, or from any other source. Put this under the first column of *Cash Inflows*.

2. Think about what you spent last week. Look at the different titles under *Cash Outflows*. Put the totals for each outflow that you have under the first column of *Cash Outflows*.

3. Under the second column of *Cash Inflows*, place the estimated amounts you expect to receive this week. Remember to include expected income from all possible sources.

4. Under the second column of *Cash Outflows*, place the estimated amounts you expect to spend for each item. There may be an item you will not have an amount for during this week. You might have an item for which you had no spending last week but for which you expect to have some this week. For example, last week there was no school dance but this week you have a school dance. Maybe you will spend more this week than last week.

CHAPTER

Budgets and Balance Sheets:
Your Personal Financial Statements

Activity #2: Creating an Annual Budget

Annual Budget

Cash Inflows	Typical Month	One Year's Cash Flow
Disposable Income (after tax)		
Allowance		
Special Event Monies (birthday money, graduation money, etc.)		
Other		
Total Cash Inflows		

Cash Outflows	Typical Month	One Year's Cash Flow
Car Payment		
Car Expenses (insurance, maintenance, and gas)		
Cell Phone		
Food (eating out and at home)		
Clothing		
Entertainment (movies, dates, etc.)		
Extra (makeup, hair products, etc.)		
Other		
Total Cash Outflows		
Net Cash Flow		

Instructions:

1. Look at your Personal Cash Flow Statement (Activity #1). You can see how much your expected net cash flow will be as you go through the month. Next, think about the whole year. Some months you might spend more (the holidays, spring break, vacation during the summer, dances, birthdays of friends and family, and so on).

2. The first column of this budget activity identifies what your expected cash inflows and outflows will be for a typical month. Using the figures you have in your personal cash flow statement for one week, determine the cash flow for one month. Put these figures in the appropriate column on the chart given.

3. To calculate your cash flow for a year, multiply each of the figures in the first column by 12. For example, if your income is $400 per month, then $400 × 12 = $4,800. So you would put $4,800 in the *Year* column for income.

CHAPTER 4

Budgets and Balance Sheets:
Your Personal Financial Statements

Activity #3: Creating a Personal Balance Sheet

Instructions:

1. Determine the value of your assets. You can do this by looking at how much money (cash) you have in your "piggy bank," checking account, and savings account. You also know the value of any other assets you might have, such as computer equipment, entertainment systems, gaming units, car, ATV, musical instruments, and so on. Put these under the *Assets* column.

2. Now you must determine if you have any liabilities. You may have a credit card or money you owe to a parent or the bank. List these next under *Liabilities*.

3. Total each section (*Assets* and *Liabilities*). To calculate your *Net Worth*, subtract your assets from your liabilities. For example, if your total assets are $1,200 and your total liabilities are $600, then your net worth would equal $600 ($1,200 – $600 = $600).

Personal Balance Sheet

Assets		Totals
Cash		
Car (and/or other vehicle)		
Entertainment System		
Computer Equipment		
Other (list)		
Total Assets		
Liabilities		
Credit Card Balance		
Outstanding Loans (bank, parents, etc.)		
Other (list)		
Total Liabilities		
Net Worth		

SCANS Foundation Skills: Basic and Thinking
SCANS Workplace Skills: Resources, Information, and Systems

CHAPTER 4

Budgets and Balance Sheets:
Your Personal Financial Statements

Activity #4: Application of Budgeting Concepts
to Your Financial Plan

Instructions:

You will need to look at the questions and respond to what is being asked. In some instances you will be given additional information.

Remember that the goal for budgeting is to help you increase your net cash flows both in the near future and distant future.

Analysis of Budget

Present Situation:

Cash Inflows =

Cash Outflows =

Net Cash Flows =

Estimated Savings per Year =

Increase Cash Inflows by:

Increasing My Income? (job?)

Increasing My Income Provided by Others Such as Allowance, Gifts, etc.

Other? (explain)

Reduce Cash Outflows by:

Reducing My Expenses? (car, vehicle(s))

_____

_____

_____

Reducing My Entertainment Expenses?

_____

_____

_____

Reducing My Other Expenses? (list)

_____

_____

_____

Conclusion (Look at the information you have provided and write what conclusions
you can draw from this concerning your budget.):

_____

_____

_____

Decisions:

Decision to Increase Net Cash Flows in the Near Future
(Look at the information you have provided and write what decision(s) you can make
to improve your cash flows in the near future.):

_____

_____

_____

Decision to Increase Net Cash Flows in the Distant Future
(Look at the information you have provided and your decision for the near future.
What decision(s) could be made to improve your cash flows in the distant future?):

_____

_____

_____

_____

CHAPTER 5

Careers and Education

VOCABULARY CHECK

1. Jonas found out the _____ for his playing in the band would be minimal.

2. Sakhone just completed an _____ at a computer repair shop.

3. Meredith wanted to be a layout specialist when she graduated. The local newspaper office told her she would need to complete an _____.

4. Adrien wanted to attend a university that had a College of Business with a recognized _____ for its program.

5. Gabriel prepared a _____ that provided a snapshot of his qualifications for a job he was interested in pursuing.

6. Cam's dad has several _____ in auto mechanics.

accreditation

apprenticeship

certification

compensation

internship

résumé

CHAPTER 5

Careers and Education

CHECK YOUR KNOWLEDGE

Multiple Choice Questions *Circle the correct answer for each of the following.*

1. Which of the following levels of education would typically result in the highest income?
   a. associate degree
   b. bachelor's degree
   c. master's degree
   d. some college, no degree

2. When making a career choice you should consider all of the following except _____.
   a. education or training required
   b. personal interests
   c. expected salary
   d. uniform required

3. One type of formalized training program that allows you to train while working is called a(n) _____.
   a. apprenticeship
   b. job
   c. clerk
   d. license

4. Information on career options can be found _____.
   a. on the Internet
   b. in books
   c. through field trips
   d. from all of these sources

5. An official document or record of an individual meeting some standard of training or knowledge is known as a _____.
   a. certification
   b. documentation
   c. skill achievement award
   d. recognition

6. A school or training program may have an official recognition known as_____ that indicates meeting a particular set of standards.
   a. certification
   b. accreditation
   c. documentation
   d. skill achievement award

7. A(n) _____ is a written snapshot of an individual's qualifications for a particular job.
   a. application
   b. résumé
   c. description
   d. paragraph

8. A résumé should contain all of the following information except _____.
   a. previous work history
   b. education
   c. family history
   d. skills and training

9. Which sector of the economy will likely experience the slowest job growth?
   a. health care
   b. services
   c. education
   d. manufacturing

10. In general, the _____ education or training you receive the _____ money you will make.
   a. more, more
   b. less, less
   c. less, more
   d. more, less

CHAPTER 5

Careers and Education

MATH CHECK UP

Instructions: *In the space provided, answer each of the following math problems. Be sure to show your work in the space provided.*

1. Lakita wants to go to trade school and study electronics for a two-year program. Her tuition and books will cost about $5,500 per year. She will also spend about $100 a month commuting from her parents' house to school. How much will her education cost her in total?

2. Shane is thinking about apprenticing as a plumber and notes that master plumbers in his region of the country make about $55,000 a year starting out. However, salaries are expected to increase by about 10 percent over the next four years. How much can Shane expect to make when his apprenticeship is over in four years?

3. Melanie has two job offers. One job pays $10 an hour and will allow her to work 40 hours a week. The other job pays $7 an hour and also requires a 40-hour week. However, the second job also pays bonuses based on sales. The other salespersons told Melanie they average about $200 a week in bonuses. Which job will likely pay the most money per week?

4. Laron is thinking about majoring in business in college because with a bachelor's degree the starting salaries are about $45,000 per year. If a master's degree will allow him to start out at about 15 percent higher, how much can he expect his starting pay to be with a master's degree?

5. Jermaine is thinking about attending college. However, he knows that he could get a job right out of high school making about $18,000 a year. He could also work part time while attending four years of college and make $7,000 a year. Assuming grants will pay for his college, how long will it take Jermaine to recover his lost wages if he chooses to go to college and will make $40,000 a year with his degree?

CHAPTER 5

Careers and Education

OPEN RESPONSE #1: Researching a Career

Please answer all parts of the question in the space provided.

Prompt: Bianca is beginning to think about what she wants to do after high school. She has come to you for help in this decision making process.

1. Identify three sources that will help her research careers. Explain how each of these will be helpful in her career search.

2. Identify three ways Bianca can get the skills needed once she has chosen her career.

Scoring Guide

4 Student gives correct answers for parts 1 and 2. All explanations are clear and complete. There is evidence of clear understanding of the concept.

3 Student gives correct answers for parts 1 and 2. Explanations are correct, but possibly unclear. There is less evidence of clear understanding.

2 Student answers 1 (1 or 2) part of the questions completely correct. There is some evidence of understanding.

1 Student gives only parts of correct answers. There is little evidence of understanding.

0 Response is totally incorrect or irrelevant (does not add any new information to the question).

_____

_____

_____

_____

_____

_____

_____

_____

_____

_____

_____

_____

_____

CHAPTER 5

Careers and Education

OPEN RESPONSE #2: Finding a Job

Please answer all parts of the question in the space provided.

Prompt: Kristopher wants to get a full-time job, but his only experience with working has been the lawn care business he began in middle school.

1. Explain to Kristopher the process of applying for a job. Explain where he can go to search for a job.

2. What three items will he need to complete? What information will Kristopher need for each item?

Scoring Guide

4 Student gives correct answers for parts 1 and 2. All explanations are clear and complete. There is evidence of clear understanding of the concept.

3 Student gives correct answers for parts 1 and 2. Explanations are correct, but possibly unclear. There is less evidence of clear understanding.

2 Student answers 1 (1 or 2) part of the questions completely correct. There is some evidence of understanding.

1 Student gives only parts of correct answers. There is little evidence of understanding.

0 Response is totally incorrect or irrelevant (does not add any new information to the question).

CHAPTER 5

Careers and Education

ACTIVITY #1: Compare Two Jobs (Careers)

Instructions:

1. Using the form provided, research two jobs of interest to you. Use all the sources available to you for your research. This can include the Internet, interviews, book sources in your library, or your guidance counselor.

2. Once you have found all your information, calculate which job will pay the most. To do this, remember to look at the salary, and include the number of hours you will work per week.

3. What are the education requirements for each job? How do these expenses figure in when you look at the opportunity costs?

_____

_____

_____

_____

_____

_____

_____

Compare Two Jobs (careers)

	Job #1:	Job #2:
Job Title (career)		
Career Cluster		
Education Requirement(s)		
Experience Required (yes or no)		
Internship or Apprenticeship (yes or no)		
Salary Range		
Job Availability		
Benefits		
Location (geographic location of available jobs in this area)		

4. Write a summary of your findings. Be sure to provide evidence to support your findings and conclusion.

_____

_____

_____

_____

_____

_____

_____

_____

_____

_____

_____

_____

_____

_____

_____

_____

_____

_____

_____

_____

_____

_____

_____

_____

_____

_____

_____

_____

_____

CHAPTER 5

Careers and Education

ACTIVITY #2: Completing a Job Application

Instructions:

1. Complete the following job application.

2. Use information that is current to you at this time. Do not make up any of the material.

3. You may also complete an online application with one of the job sites such as **www.Monster.com**. If you use one of these sites, please have your teacher or parent (guardian) check the information before you post the application online.

PERSONAL INFORMATION

First Name: _____ Middle Name: _____

Last Name: _____

Street Address: _____

City, State, Zip Code: _____

Phone Number: (   ) _____

Are you eligible to work in the United States?   Y   N

If you are under age 18, do you have an employment/age certificate?   Y   N

Have you been convicted of a felony within the last five years?   Y   N

If yes, please explain: _____

_____

POSITION/AVAILABILITY

Position Applied For: _____

Days Available: Hours Available (inlcude a.m./p.m.):

Monday	Y	N	From	to
Tuesday	Y	N	From	to
Wednesday	Y	N	From	to
Thursday	Y	N	From	to
Friday	Y	N	From	to
Saturday	Y	N	From	to

Sunday   Y   N   From   to

What date are you available to start work?

EDUCATION

Name and Address of School	Degree/Diploma	Graduation Date

Skills and Qualifications (licenses, skills, training, awards):

EMPLOYMENT HISTORY

Present or Last Position:

Employer:

Address:

Supervisor:

Phone:

E-mail:

Position Title:

From: To:

Responsibilities:

Salary:

If this is your present employer, may we contact your employer?   Y   N

If this is your former employer, what was your reason for leaving?

Previous Position:

Employer:

Address:

Supervisor:

Phone:

E-mail:

Position Title:

From: To:

Responsibilities:

Salary:

Reason for Leaving:

References (Name, title, company, address, phone, email):

I certify that information contained in this application is true and complete. I understand that false information may be grounds for not hiring me or for immediate termination of employment at any point in the future if I am hired. I authorize the verification of all information listed above.

Signature: Date:

CHAPTER 5

Careers and Education

ACTIVITY #3: Preparing a Résumé

Instructions:

1. Gather the information needed for your résumé. Remember, this needs to be a résumé that represents you at this time. Do not make up any of the details. This is a snapshot of who you are for potential employers.

2. Use the sample provided in the chapter to help you format your résumé. You may also use résumé software or a résumé aid located on word processing software.

3. Develop a separate page for your references.

CHAPTER 5

Careers and Education

ACTIVITY #4: Preparing a Cover Letter

Instructions:

1. Look through the newspaper or online for a job that interests you.

2. Use this job advertisement to write a cover letter applying for the job.

3. Follow the example provided in the chapter to write your cover letter.

4. Begin your cover letter by designing your letterhead. Be sure to not use graphics or pictures. You want to present a very professional image of yourself. Your letterhead needs to provide contact information for you. You will have your name, the address at which the employer can contact you, phone contact number (home and a cell phone number if applicable), and an e-mail address (if desired).

5. Use the current date for your cover letter.

6. Use your teacher/instructor's name and school address for your mailing address.

7. In the body of the letter be sure to follow these guidelines:
   a. The first paragraph needs to inform how you found out about the job.
      i. newspaper
      ii. online
      iii. word of mouth (another employee, etc.)
   b. The next paragraph (or two) needs to tell what your qualifications are for the job.
   c. The closing paragraph needs to be positive. You might also want to provide preferred contact times and numbers.

SCANS Foundation Skills: Basic, Thinking, and Personal
SCANS Workplace Skills: Resources, Information, Systems, and Technology

61

CHAPTER 6

Paying Taxes

VOCABULARY CHECK

1. Gera's _____ was less than what she expected because of all the taxes that were taken out.

2. Matthew had to pay _____ on the car he purchased.

3. Money collected by the government for the purpose of operating the government is called a _____.

4. If Robin multiplied her hourly wage by the number of hours she worked, she would be able to figure her _____.

5. Bobby's employer was required to withhold _____ on all the employees at the pizza parlor and pay that amount to the government every quarter.

6. To find out more about paying taxes, Horace went to the _____ Web site.

7. Amanda had to file a _____ before April 15 on her earnings from her job at the gym.

8. Colin found out that FICA was money withheld and sent to the government that funded _____ and _____ for retirees.

9. The taxes imposed on Milad's earnings reflect his _____.

10. The first step for Amanda to calculate how much federal tax she owes was to determine her _____. This would be her income from almost any source, especially her job at the gym.

11. Dillon's dad sold stock for a profit and had to report the _____ on his tax return.

12. Amanda needed to calculate her _____ and _____ for her tax return to determine which method would give her the smallest tax liability.

13. Robin's mother reminded her that her _____ would not be the same as her gross pay because taxes would be taken out.

14. Amanda's _____ was figured after she subtracted her allowable amounts, such as moving expenses and student loan interest paid, from her total income.

adjusted gross income

capital gain

gross income

gross pay

Internal Revenue Service

itemized deduction

Medicare

net pay

payroll tax

personal income tax

sales tax

Social Security

standard deduction

take-home pay

tax

tax return

CHAPTER 6

Paying Taxes

CHECK YOUR KNOWLEDGE

Multiple Choice Questions *Circle the correct answer for each of the following.*

1. Money collected from individuals and corporations by some branch of the government is known as (a) _____.
   a. tax
   b. net pay
   c. gross pay
   d. fundage

2. A synonym for take-home pay is _____.
   a. gross pay
   b. tax
   c. FICA
   d. net pay

3. Payroll taxes can include all of the following except _____.
   a. state income tax
   b. sales tax
   c. federal income tax
   d. FICA

4. The federal tax system is carried out by the _____.
   a. Internal Revenue Service
   b. Federal Deposit Insurance Corporation
   c. Federal Taxation Office
   d. U.S. Treasury

5. By law federal tax returns must be filed by what date?
   a. January 1
   b. December 31
   c. May 2
   d. April 15

6. A(n) _____ formally reports your tax information to the federal government.
   a. confirmation letter
   b. tax return
   c. payroll stub
   d. income report

7. Which of the following is not a possible filing status used when filing your federal income tax return?
   a. single
   b. head of household
   c. siblings filing jointly
   d. married filing separate return

8. For tax purposes, if you sell an asset for more than you paid for it, you will have what is called a(n) _____.
   a. capital gain
   b. tax deduction
   c. tax credit
   d. capital loss

9. Gross income includes all of the following except _____.
   a. tips
   b. child support payments received
   c. wages
   d. game show winnings

10. Taxes impact all of the following financial decisions except _____.
   a. whether to rent or buy
   b. where to live
   c. investment options
   d. the type of clothing to wear

CHAPTER 6

Paying Taxes

MATH CHECK UP

Instructions: *In the space provided, answer each of the following math problems. Be sure to show your work in the space provided.*

1. Jesse worked forty hours this past week. Assuming he makes $12 an hour, how much was withheld from his check by his employer for FICA if FICA withholdings were 7.65%.?

2. Marlin made $557 in gross pay. His employer withheld $88.25 in total federal tax, state tax, and FICA from his check. How much was his net pay?

3. Ramek sold 100 shares of stock for $58 a share. He paid $49 a share for it three years ago. How much was his capital gain?

4. How much will Kasey pay in Medicare if she makes $42,300 next year?

5. How much will Laura bring home if she makes $745 a week if 7.65 percent is withheld for FICA and 12 percent is withheld for federal and state tax?

CHAPTER 6

Paying Taxes

OPEN RESPONSE #1: What's on a Pay Stub

Please answer all parts of the question in the space provided.

Prompt: Sarah Beth just got her first paycheck. There is less money than she was expecting. Sarah Beth has asked you to look at her check to explain why there is less money. Specifically, she wants to know what is this FICA that has come out of her check!

1. Explain FICA to Sarah Beth. Tell her why it is important that FICA be withheld even at a minimum-wage job.

2. Explain to Sarah Beth the different parts of her pay stub.

Scoring Guide

4 Student gives correct answers for parts 1 and 2. All explanations are clear and complete. There is evidence of clear understanding of the concept.

3 Student gives correct answers for parts 1 and 2. Explanations are correct, but possibly unclear. There is less evidence of clear understanding.

2 Student answers 1 (1 or 2) part of the questions completely correct. There is some evidence of understanding.

1 Student gives only parts of correct answers. There is little evidence of understanding.

0 Response is totally incorrect or irrelevant (does not add any new information to the question).

_____

_____

_____

_____

_____

_____

_____

_____

_____

_____

_____

_____

Paying Taxes

OPEN RESPONSE #2: Filling out a 1040EZ

Please answer all parts of the question in the space provided.

Prompt: You have a friend who is going to file a tax return for the first time. Your friend is unsure where to begin and shows you a 1040EZ form and her W-2.

1. Explain to your friend where the information on her W-2 is placed on the 1040EZ form.

2. Explain what decision(s) she will need to make as she is filling out the 1040EZ form.

Scoring Guide

4 Student gives correct answers for parts 1 and 2. All explanations are clear and complete. There is evidence of clear understanding of the concept.

3 Student gives correct answers for parts 1 and 2. Explanations are correct, but possibly unclear. There is less evidence of clear understanding.

2 Student answers 1 (1 or 2) part of the questions completely correct. There is some evidence of understanding.

1 Student gives only parts of correct answers. There is little evidence of understanding.

0 Response is totally incorrect or irrelevant (does not add any new information to the question).

_____

_____

_____

_____

_____

_____

_____

_____

_____

_____

_____

_____

_____

_____

CHAPTER 6

Paying Taxes

ACTIVITY #1: Filling out the Information in a Pay Stub

Instructions:

1. Use the following pay information to complete the pay stub. Imagine this is the last pay period for the tax year.

    Hours worked = 40; Regular pay = $400; Year-to-date = $8,420; FICA =$24.80; FICA YTD= $522.04; Medicare = $5.80; Medicare YTD = $122.09; Federal tax = $40; Federal tax YTD = $842; net pay = 329.40; and YTD net pay = $6,933.87.

Hours Worked	
Regular Pay	
FICA	
Medicare	
Federal Tax	
Net Pay	
Pay YTD	
FICA YTD	
Medicare YTD	
Federal Tax YTD	
Net Pay YTD	

2. How can you be sure that there are no mistakes on your pay stub assuming you make $10 an hour and your employer withholds 10 percent for federal taxes? Write a paragraph explaining how to calculate your gross pay for one week, your net pay, and why there is a difference.

_____

_____

_____

_____

_____

_____

SCANS Foundation Skills: Basic and Thinking

SCANS Workplace Skills: Resources, Information, and Systems

CHAPTER 6

Paying Taxes

ACTIVITY #2: Completing a W-2 Form

Instructions:

1. Using the information provided, fill out the W-2.

Jim Anybody (Box e)

Please include the following data in the boxes, as indicated:

Box a: xxx-xx-xxxx

Box b: xx-xxxxxxx

Box c: Larry's Lawn Care
        555 Main Street
        Anytown, USA 12345

Box d: xx

Box e: Their Name
        444 Main Street
        Anytown, USA 12345

Box 1: 8,420.00

Box 2: empty

Box 3: 8,420.00

Box 4: 522.04

Box 5: 8,420.00

Box 6: 92.80

Boxes 7–14—all empty

Box 15: MA (no need to include state ID number)

Box 16: 8,420.00

Box 17–20: Empty

You will also need to provide the employee name. Use xxx-xx-xxxx for the Social Security number.

22222	Void ☐	**a** Employee's social security number	For Official Use Only ⑧ OMB No. 1545-0008	
b Employer identification number (EIN)			**1** Wages, tips, other compensation	**2** Federal income tax withheld
c Employer's name, address, and ZIP code			**3** Social security wages	**4** Social security tax withheld
			5 Medicare wages and tips	**6** Medicare tax withheld
			7 Social security tips	**8** Allocated tips
d Control number			**9**	**10** Dependent care benefits
e Employee's first name and initial	Last name	Suff.	**11** Nonqualified plans	**12a** See instructions for box 12
			13 Statutory employee ☐ Retirement plan ☐ Third-party sick pay ☐	**12b**
			14 Other	**12c**
				12d
f Employee's address and ZIP code				

15 State Employer's state ID number	**16** State wages, tips, etc.	**17** State income tax	**18** Local wages, tips, etc.	**19** Local income tax	**20** Locality name

Form W-2 Wage and Tax Statement **2011**

Department of the Treasury—Internal Revenue Service

Copy A For Social Security Administration — Send this entire page with Form W-3 to the Social Security Administration; photocopies are **not** acceptable.

For Privacy Act and Paperwork Reduction Act Notice, see back of Copy D.

Cat. No. 10134D

Do Not Cut, Fold, or Staple Forms on This Page — Do Not Cut, Fold, or Staple Forms on This Page

2. Write a paragraph that explains what a W-2 is and when you receive this from your employer.

_____

_____

_____

_____

_____

_____

_____

_____

_____

_____

_____

_____

_____

_____

_____

_____

_____

_____

_____

_____

_____

_____

_____

_____

_____

_____

_____

_____

_____

_____

_____

CHAPTER 6

Paying Taxes

ACTIVITY #3: Preparing a 1040EZ

Instructions:

1. Using the information from Activity #2 (W-2 form), complete the 1040EZ provided on the following pages. Use the tax tables at the following online location to calculate tax liability: **http://www.irs.gov/pub/irs-pdf/i1040ez.pdf**

2. Write a paragraph explaining what information is needed to complete a 1040EZ, when it is required to be turned in, and who will need to pay more taxes, who will not, and who will receive a refund.

_____

_____

_____

_____

_____

_____

_____

_____

_____

_____

_____

_____

_____

_____

_____

_____

_____

_____

_____

_____

_____

_____

SCANS Foundation Skills: Basic, Thinking, and Personal

SCANS Workplace Skills: Resources, Information, Systems, and Technology

Form 1040EZ

Income Tax Return for Single and Joint Filers With No Dependents (99)

2011

OMB No. 1545-0074

Your first name and initial	Last name	Your social security number

If a joint return, spouse's first name and initial	Last name	Spouse's social security number

Home address (number and street). If you have a P.O. box, see instructions.	Apt. no.	▲ Make sure the SSN(s) above are correct.

City, town or post office, state, and ZIP code. If you have a foreign address, also complete spaces below (see instructions).

Presidential Election Campaign
Check here if you, or your spouse if filing jointly, want $3 to go to this fund. Checking a box below will not change your tax or refund. ☐ You ☐ Spouse

Foreign country name	Foreign province/county	Foreign postal code

Income

Attach Form(s) W-2 here.

Enclose, but do not attach, any payment.

1 Wages, salaries, and tips. This should be shown in box 1 of your Form(s) W-2. Attach your Form(s) W-2. — **1**

2 Taxable interest. If the total is over $1,500, you cannot use Form 1040EZ. — **2**

3 Unemployment compensation and Alaska Permanent Fund dividends (see instructions). — **3**

4 Add lines 1, 2, and 3. This is your **adjusted gross income.** — **4**

5 If someone can claim you (or your spouse if a joint return) as a dependent, check the applicable box(es) below and enter the amount from the worksheet on back.

☐ You ☐ Spouse

If no one can claim you (or your spouse if a joint return), enter $9,500 if **single;** $19,000 if **married filing jointly.** See back for explanation. — **5**

6 Subtract line 5 from line 4. If line 5 is larger than line 4, enter -0-. This is your **taxable income.** ▶ **6**

Payments, Credits, and Tax

7 Federal income tax withheld from Form(s) W-2 and 1099. — **7**

8a **Earned income credit (EIC)** (see instructions). — **8a**

b Nontaxable combat pay election. **8b**

9 Add lines 7 and 8a. These are your **total payments and credits.** ▶ **9**

10 **Tax.** Use the amount on **line 6 above** to find your tax in the tax table in the instructions. Then, enter the tax from the table on this line. — **10**

Refund

Have it directly deposited! See instructions and fill in 11b, 11c, and 11d or Form 8888.

11a If line 9 is larger than line 10, subtract line 10 from line 9. This is your **refund.** If Form 8888 is attached, check here ▶ ☐ — **11a**

▶ **b** Routing number ▶ **c** Type: ☐ Checking ☐ Savings

▶ **d** Account number

Amount You Owe

12 If line 10 is larger than line 9, subtract line 9 from line 10. This is the **amount you owe.** For details on how to pay, see instructions. ▶ **12**

Third Party Designee

Do you want to allow another person to discuss this return with the IRS (see instructions)? ☐ **Yes.** Complete below. ☐ **No**

Designee's name ▶	Phone no. ▶	Personal identification number (PIN) ▶

Sign Here

Under penalties of perjury, I declare that I have examined this return and, to the best of my knowledge and belief, it is true, correct, and accurately lists all amounts and sources of income I received during the tax year. Declaration of preparer (other than the taxpayer) is based on all information of which the preparer has any knowledge.

Joint return? See instructions.

Keep a copy for your records.

Your signature	Date	Your occupation	Daytime phone number
Spouse's signature. If a joint return, **both** must sign.	Date	Spouse's occupation	If the IRS sent you an Identity Protection PIN, enter it here (see inst.)

Paid Preparer Use Only

Print/Type preparer's name	Preparer's signature	Date	Check ☐ if self-employed	PTIN
Firm's name ▶		Firm's EIN ▶		
Firm's address ▶		Phone no.		

For Disclosure, Privacy Act, and Paperwork Reduction Act Notice, see instructions.   Cat. No. 11329W   Form **1040EZ** (2011)

Use this form if	• Your filing status is single or married filing jointly. If you are not sure about your filing status, see instructions. • You (and your spouse if married filing jointly) were under age 65 and not blind at the end of 2011. If you were born on January 1, 1947, you are considered to be age 65 at the end of 2011. • You do not claim any dependents. For information on dependents, see Pub. 501. • Your taxable income (line 6) is less than $100,000. • You do not claim any adjustments to income. For information on adjustments to income, use TeleTax topics 451–453 and 455–458 (see instructions). • The only tax credit you can claim is the earned income credit (EIC). The credit may give you a refund even if you do not owe any tax. You do not need a qualifying child to claim the EIC. For information on credits, use TeleTax topics 601, 602, 607, 608, 610, 611, and 612 (see instructions). • You had only wages, salaries, tips, taxable scholarship or fellowship grants, unemployment compensation, or Alaska Permanent Fund dividends, and your taxable interest was not over $1,500. But if you earned tips, including allocated tips, that are not included in box 5 and box 7 of your Form W-2, you may not be able to use Form 1040EZ (see instructions). If you are planning to use Form 1040EZ for a child who received Alaska Permanent Fund dividends, see instructions.
Filling in your return	If you received a scholarship or fellowship grant or tax-exempt interest income, such as on municipal bonds, see the instructions before filling in the form. Also, see the instructions if you received a Form 1099-INT showing federal income tax withheld or if federal income tax was withheld from your unemployment compensation or Alaska Permanent Fund dividends.
For tips on how to avoid common mistakes, see instructions.	Remember, you must report all wages, salaries, and tips even if you do not get a Form W-2 from your employer. You must also report all your taxable interest, including interest from banks, savings and loans, credit unions, etc., even if you do not get a Form 1099-INT.

Worksheet for Line 5 — Dependents Who Checked One or Both Boxes	Use this worksheet to figure the amount to enter on line 5 if someone can claim you (or your spouse if married filing jointly) as a dependent, even if that person chooses not to do so. To find out if someone can claim you as a dependent, see Pub. 501.
	
	A. Amount, if any, from line 1 on front . . . . $\underline{\qquad + \qquad 300.00 \quad}$ Enter total ▶ **A.** $\underline{\qquad\qquad}$
	B. Minimum standard deduction . . . . **B.** $\underline{\qquad 950.00}$
	C. Enter the **larger** of line A or line B here . . . . **C.** $\underline{\qquad\qquad}$
	D. Maximum standard deduction. If **single**, enter $5,800; if **married filing jointly**, enter $11,600 . **D.** $\underline{\qquad\qquad}$
	E. Enter the **smaller** of line C or line D here. This is your standard deduction . . . . **E.** $\underline{\qquad\qquad}$
	F. Exemption amount.
	   • If single, enter -0-.
	   • If married filing jointly and —
	     —both you and your spouse can be claimed as dependents, enter -0-.
	     —only one of you can be claimed as a dependent, enter $3,700. **F.** $\underline{\qquad\qquad}$
	G. Add lines E and F. Enter the total here and on line 5 on the front . . . . **G.** $\underline{\qquad\qquad}$

(keep a copy for your records)	**If you did not check any boxes on line 5,** enter on line 5 the amount shown below that applies to you. • Single, enter $9,500. This is the total of your standard deduction ($5,800) and your exemption ($3,700). • Married filing jointly, enter $19,000. This is the total of your standard deduction ($11,600), your exemption ($3,700), and your spouse's exemption ($3,700).

Mailing Return	Mail your return by **April 17, 2012.** Mail it to the address shown on the last page of the instructions.

Form **1040EZ** (2011)

CHAPTER 7

Insuring Your Health and Your Life

VOCABULARY CHECK

1. Tabitha worked for a year before going to technical school but now she knew what she wanted to do with her life. When she quit her job and enrolled in school she also signed up for _____ offered by the school since she was no longer covered through work.

2. Al looked into buying health _____ for himself through his employer.

3. The _____ on car insurance for Ted was going to go up with the purchase of a newer car.

4. Anthony's grandparents were on _____ because they were over 65 years old.

5. Anthony's young cousins were eligible for _____ since they lived with his grandparents.

6. Tricia was the _____ for her family's health insurance policy that was purchased through her employer.

7. Because Jontell did not have health insurance when she was injured, an insurance company would consider her injury now a _____.

8. Trey's father participates in a _____ offered at work.

9. When Bethany had to have knee surgery for a basketball injury, her parents were responsible for the first $500 of the cost because their previous claims had not met the _____ on the insurance.

10. Curt's _____ or co-pay for his doctor's visit was $20.

11. Theresa received money from her grandfather's _____ policy upon his death since she was listed as a _____.

12. Tera's _____ was part of her financial plan as an investment.

13. Two other types of life insurance that can be purchased are: _____, which builds no saving and does not serve as an investment, and _____, which builds savings and is more flexible.

14. When Tabitha's father changed jobs, he knew that _____ would ensure he would be able to get health insurance through his new job.

beneficiary

COBRA

co-insurance

deductible

disability insurance

fraud

group plan

health insurance

HIPAA

insurance

liability

life insurance

Medicaid

Medicare

policyholder

preexisting condition

premium

term insurance

universal life insurance

whole life insurance

15. Terrence's father lost his job but because of _____ he was able to keep buying health insurance through his old employer for up to 18 months until he found a new job.

16. Filing a false claim, a type of insurance _____ can make costs soar.

17. Jamal owed the hospital $1,200 from his surgery last year. When he went to borrow money to buy a car he had to list this debt as a _____.

18. Efi purchased _____ to provide income in the event illness or injury made it impossible for him to work and earn a living.

CHAPTER 7

Insuring Your Health and Your Life
CHECK YOUR KNOWLEDGE

Multiple Choice Questions *Circle the correct answer for each of the following.*

1. A regular payment made to purchase insurance coverage is known as a _____.
   a. premium
   b. reduction
   c. billable
   d. monetary award

2. A government-sponsored program designed to provide health insurance for low-income individuals is called _____.
   a. Social Security
   b. Internal Revenue Service
   c. Medicaid
   d. sponsorship

3. In general, health-care costs have been _____ in recent years.
   a. decreasing
   b. constant
   c. stagnant
   d. increasing

4. Health care plans that allow members to seek health care from any medical provider are known as _____.
   a. managed care plans
   b. health seeker plans
   c. indemnity plans
   d. participant plans

5. Health-insurance plans may limit coverage based on all of the following factors except _____.
   a. gender
   b. location where the care is provided
   c. preexisting conditions
   d. length of hospital stay

6. When an insured person shares in the cost of a specific treatment at the time it is rendered, it is known as a(n) _____.
   a. premium
   b. co-pay
   c. provider
   d. expanded cost

7. A _____ is the designated recipient of the proceeds of a life insurance policy.
  a. beneficiary
  b. designator
  c. relative
  d. policyholder

8. Life insurance that provides coverage for a set period of time *and* builds savings for the policyholder is called _____.
  a. term life
  b. whole life
  c. universal life
  d. dedicated life

9. Life insurance coverage is sometimes provided by your _____.
  a. employer
  b. school
  c. occupation
  d. local government

10. The legislation that ensures you can transfer jobs and still gain access to health insurance at your new job is known as _____.
  a. FICA
  b. HIPAA
  c. COBRA
  d. PPO

CHAPTER 7

Insuring Your Health and Your Life
MATH CHECK UP

Instructions: *In the space provided, answer each of the following math problems. Be sure to show your work in the space provided.*

1. Naomi's new employer offered her health insurance coverage for $95 per month. However, she was also offered the option to cover her husband and two children for $376 a month. How much would it cost her annually to add her family to her health insurance?

2. Owen is planning surgery to repair the torn ligament in his knee. The total cost of the surgery is expected to be about $7,000. Owen has a $1,000 deductible and then a 20 percent co-pay for this procedure. How much will Owen pay for his part of the surgery?

3. Mikel's dental insurance will pay up to 80 percent of the cost of a root canal and 50 percent of the cost of the crown. However, overall coverage is limited to $1,000 in total payments. Assuming the root canal will cost $1,200 and the crown will cost $1,000, how much will Mikel have to pay to get this tooth fixed?

4. If Brandon, Tony, and Scott are all listed as equal beneficiaries on their aunt's $500,000 life insurance policy, how much should each receive in the event of her death?

5. Zeb's health insurance premium is supposed to increase by 12 percent next year. Assuming he currently pays $111 a month for coverage, how much will he pay next year?

CHAPTER 7

Insuring Your Health and Your Life
OPEN RESPONSE #1: Finding Health Insurance

Please answer all parts of the question in the space provided.

Prompt: Sue Ann is putting together her financial plan. Her parents told her to be sure to include insurance as part of that plan. She knows that you have a financial plan already in place and wants advice from you about including insurance in your financial plan.

1. List three sources of health insurance. Explain the difference in each of these and how they will affect her financial plan.

2. List three health insurance features Sue Ann should consider. Explain each of these features.

Scoring Guide

4 Student gives correct answers for parts 1 and 2. All explanations are clear and complete. There is evidence of clear understanding of the concept.

3 Student gives correct answers for parts 1 and 2. Explanations are correct, but possibly unclear. There is less evidence of clear understanding.

2 Student answers 1 (1 or 2) part of the questions completely correct. There is some evidence of understanding.

1 Student gives only parts of correct answers. There is little evidence of understanding.

0 Response is totally incorrect or irrelevant (does not add any new information to the question).

CHAPTER 7

Insuring Your Health and Your Life
OPEN RESPONSE #2: Finding Life Insurance

Please answer all parts of the question in the space provided.

Prompt: As Sue Ellen begins planning for health insurance in her financial plan, she hears about life insurance. Sue Ellen asks you how you included life insurance in your financial plan.

1. Explain to Sue Ellen the importance of life insurance and the role it plays in your financial plan.

2. What are the three types of life insurance Sue Ellen will need to examine? Explain each and how they will affect her financial plan.

Scoring Guide

4 Student gives correct answers for parts 1 and 2. All explanations are clear and complete. There is evidence of clear understanding of the concept.

3 Student gives correct answers for parts 1 and 2. Explanations are correct, but possibly unclear. There is less evidence of clear understanding.

2 Student answers 1 (1 or 2) part of the questions completely correct. There is some evidence of understanding.

1 Student gives only parts of correct answers. There is little evidence of understanding.

0 Response is totally incorrect or irrelevant (does not add any new information to the question).

_____

_____

_____

_____

_____

_____

_____

_____

_____

_____

_____

_____

_____

CHAPTER 7

Insuring Your Health and Your Life

ACTIVITY #1: Compare Cost of Two Insurance Policies

Instructions:

1. Using the form provided, research the cost of individual health insurance versus a group plan. Use all the sources available to you for your research. This can include the Internet, interviews with family members who belong to a group plan, book sources in your library, and your local insurance agent.

Compare Two Insurance Policies

	Individual (Private) Insurance	Group Plan (Employer) Insurance
Cost per Person		
Family Plan Cost		
Services Covered		
PPO, HMO, or Other		
Co-insurance Costs (co-pay)		

2. Write a summary of your findings. Be sure to provide evidence to support your findings and conclusions. In your summary, explain how each of these would affect your financial plan.

_____

_____

_____

_____

_____

_____

_____

_____

SCANS Foundation Skills: Basic and Thinking

SCANS Workplace Skills: Resources, Information, and Systems

CHAPTER 7

Insuring Your Health and Your Life

ACTIVITY #2: Comparing the Three Types of Life Insurance

Instructions:

1. Using the form provided, research the cost of the three types of life insurance. Use all the sources available to you for your research. This can include the Internet, interviews, book sources in your library, and your local insurance agent.

	Whole Life Insurance	Term Insurance	Universal Life Insurance
Cost (premium)			
Builds Savings (yes or no)			
Period of Time (how long they provide coverage)			
Benefits (payment at death or other)			

2. Write a summary of your findings. In your summary, explain how each of these would affect your financial plan. Be sure to provide evidence to support your findings and conclusions.

_____

_____

_____

_____

_____

_____

_____

_____

SCANS Foundation Skills: Basic, Thinking, and Personal

SCANS Workplace Skills: Resources, Information, Systems, and Technology

CHAPTER 8

The Economy and You
VOCABULARY CHECK

1. The decisions that we make every day are matters of _____, or the study of choices.

2. Analyzing characteristics of groups of people, for example their race, education, gender, and age, is called _____, or the study of human populations.

3. The overall system in which we see the interaction of different people and groups is known as the _____.

4. The period between 1946 and 1964 characterized by high birth rates in the United States is called the _____, which helps to explain the "graying of America."

5. The _____ reflects the total dollar amount of all final goods and services purchased in a given year.

6. A _____ is one full period of economic growth followed by a period of recession.

7. CPI stands for _____, which is constructed from price data collected from about 300 goods and services that most people consume during the year.

baby boom
business cycle
consumer price index
demographics
depression
economics
economy
global economy
gross domestic product
inflation
macroeconomics
microeconomics
recession

8. A period when the economy is shrinking is known as a _____.

9. An economy in which many of the world's countries interact and depend on each other is known as a _____.

10. A study of broad issues that impact the economy as a whole is known as _____.

11. A sustained increase in the general level of prices, such as gasoline, clothing, and other items, is known as _____.

12. A severe recession is known as a _____.

13. The study of individual choices or decisions made by smaller units, such as a computer firm, is known as _____.

CHAPTER 8

The Economy and You
CHECK YOUR KNOWLEDGE

Multiple Choice Questions *Circle the correct answer for each of the following.*

1. The study of human population characteristics is called _____.
   a. population studies
   b. demographics
   c. census data
   d. politics

2. People born in the United States between 1946 and 1964 are known as _____.
   a. baby boomers
   b. baby busters
   c. Generation X
   d. Generation Y

3. The government measures economic activity by calculating the _____.
   a. consumer price index
   b. consumer sentiment
   c. gross domestic product
   d. inflation rate

4. A period of time in which the economy is shrinking is known as a _____.
   a. boom
   b. stable economy
   c. slide
   d. recession

5. A sustained increase in the general level of prices is known as _____.
   a. recession
   b. inflation
   c. deflation
   d. depression

6. Inflation is measured by changes in the _____.
   a. gross domestic product
   b. consumer sentiment index
   c. consumer price index
   d. recessionary inflator

7. The study of choices is often called _____.
   a. demographics
   b. economics
   c. recession
   d. globalization

8. When economics focuses on factors affecting the broader economy, it is called
_____.

    a. macroeconomics

    b. microeconomics

    c. globalization

    d. governmental economics

9. A severe recession is known as a(n) _____.

    a. phase

    b. depression

    c. cycle disturbance

    d. inflation

10. The global economy refers to _____.

    a. tourism spending

    b. travel to other countries

    c. immigration issues

    d. economic interdependence among countries

CHAPTER 8

The Economy and You
MATH CHECK UP

Instructions: *In the space provided, answer each of the following math problems. Be sure to show your work in the space provided.*

1. Yolanda would like to attend a 12-month program that will certify her as a court reporter. The program costs $8,500 in tuition, fees, and books and will allow her to make about $31,250 a year when she becomes certified. She will not have time to work during the year of training. Assuming she could make $18,000 a year without the training, how long will it take her to recoup her investment?

2. If the population of the United States grows by 4 percent next year and it is currently estimated to be about 310 million people, what is the expected population?

3. Assuming that there are 95 million workers in the labor force in 2030 and 55 million retirees drawing Social Security, how many workers will be paying in per retiree at that time?

4. If the gross domestic product is currently 15,290 billion dollars and grows by 5 percent, how much will it be next year?

5. If annual inflation is 4 percent, how much will it cost on December 31 to buy goods that you paid $20 for on January 1 at the beginning of the year?

CHAPTER 8

The Economy and You

OPEN RESPONSE #1: Economics and Choices

Please answer all parts of the question in the space provided.

Prompt: Gerald is trying to understand what economics is all about. He understands it is about choices that are made, but he is unclear what kind of choices are involved. Gerald also does not understand what economics has to do with his personal financial plan.

1. Explain to Gerald how economic choices could affect his personal financial plan. Give two examples to help support your explanation.

2. Explain to Gerald how economics is broken into two categories and describe both categories.

Scoring Guide

4 Student gives correct answers for parts 1 and 2. All explanations are clear and complete. There is evidence of clear understanding of the concept.

3 Student gives correct answers for parts 1 and 2. Explanations are correct, but possibly unclear. There is less evidence of clear understanding.

2 Student answers 1 (1 or 2) part of the questions completely correct. There is some evidence of understanding.

1 Student gives only parts of correct answers. There is little evidence of understanding.

0 Response is totally incorrect or irrelevant (does not add any new information to the question).

CHAPTER 8

The Economy and You

OPEN RESPONSE #2: What Is Your Demographic Group?

Please answer all parts of the question in the space provided.

Prompt: Crissandra, who is 17, wants to understand where she fits in the demographics of the country, but first she needs to understand what demographics means. She has heard the phrase "the graying of America." What she does not know is how this information affects her personal financial plan.

1. Explain to Crissandra two factors that are considered in a discussion of demographics. Give two examples to support the discussion.

2. Explain to Crissandra where she fits in the breakdown of demographic groups. Give two other demographic groups and examples of who might be in each of these groups.

3. Explain the phrase "the graying of America" and how this information may affect her personal financial plan.

Scoring Guide

4 Student gives correct answers for parts 1–3. All explanations are clear and complete. There is evidence of clear understanding of the concept.

3 Student gives correct answers for parts 1–3. Explanations are correct, but possibly unclear. There is less evidence of clear understanding.

2 Student fails to answer at least one of the parts correctly. There is some evidence of understanding.

1 Student gives only parts of correct answers. There is little evidence of understanding.

0 Response is totally incorrect or irrelevant (does not add any new information to the question).

SCANS Foundation Skills: Basic and Thinking
SCANS Workplace Skills: Resources and Interpersonal Information

CHAPTER 8

The Economy and You

ACTIVITY #1: Compare Three Demographic Groups

Instructions:

1. Using the form provided, research three people who fit into three of the generational demographic groups. This may be someone in your family, family friends, someone famous, or someone in your school.

   You will need to research key events that shaped the world during each person's childhood and young adulthood—the period between their birth and the age at which they would have had their own children. Use all the sources available to you for your research. This can include the Internet, interviews, book sources in your library, and your guidance counselor.

Compare Three Different Demographic Groups

	Group #1	Group #2	Group #3
Name			
Demographic Group			
Event #1 of This Period			
Event #2 of This Period			
Event #3 of This Period			

2. Once you have located your information, develop a timeline showing the different generations. In your timeline, be sure to show the important events of each generation. Your timeline design is of your choosing, as long as the information you have found is presented on the timeline.

3. Write a description of your timeline. Be sure to provide examples in your description.

_____

_____

_____

_____

_____

_____

SCANS Foundation Skills: Basic and Thinking
SCANS Workplace Skills: Resources, Information, and Systems

CHAPTER 8

The Economy and You

ACTIVITY #2: The Global Economy

Instructions:

1. Research five products to find out where these products were produced. Look into where the service contracts for these products are fulfilled. For example, do customers call someone in the United States when they call the service center or 800 number of the product for help? Find out all you can about each product and its production.

   Use all the sources available to you for your research. This can include the Internet, interviews, book sources in your library, or local retailers.

2. Once you have found your information, develop a chart that shows your findings. The design of this chart may be completed using technology, paper/pencil, or cut/paste. Be creative.

3. Write a narrative about your chart.

_____

_____

_____

_____

_____

_____

_____

_____

_____

_____

_____

_____

_____

_____

_____

_____

_____

_____

_____

SCANS Foundation Skills: Basic, Thinking, and Personal

SCANS Workplace Skills: Resources, Information, Systems, and Technology

CHAPTER 9

Obtaining and Protecting Your Credit
VOCABULARY CHECK

1. Sebastian wanted to apply for _____ to get his new guitar, but the _____ rate was high.

2. Brandy had trouble getting credit because she had never applied for credit and she had no _____.

3. Bryna was a victim of _____ when someone opened up a credit account in her name.

4. Brandy's father explained that the loan on her car was a type of _____ and that her payments would be due every month on the same date until her loan was paid off.

5. Bryce was trying to purchase music online when he was redirected to a site that appeared to be official but that he soon discovered was not. He was about to be a victim of
_____.

6. Luther knew that creditors could not deny him credit based on his ethnicity or race because of the _____.

7. Credit cards are an example of _____.

8. Ebony saw the ad for "30 days, same as cash" and thought this option would work well for her. This type of credit in which monthly or weekly payments may not be required is known as
_____.

9. Dustin requested his _____ from TransUnion, which is a _____.

10. Kenzie knows he has a good _____ because he saw his credit report. This score is based on a model created by
_____.

11. Claude worried that someone was _____ when he was getting money at the ATM.

12. Dwight's mother was a victim of _____ when a hotel employee copied her credit card number during her last business trip.

13. Kaitlin received an email that appeared to be from her bank requesting that she verify account information. This type of fraud is called _____.

14. Cody had $500 showing as his _____ left on the loan.

15. Jonathan asked that his _____ be increased on his credit card to $500.

credit
credit bureau
credit history
credit limit
credit report
credit score
creditor
Equal Credit Opportunity Act
Fair Credit Reporting Act
Fair Isaac Corporation
identity theft
installment credit
interest
noninstallment credit
pharming
phishing
pretexting
principal
revolving open-end credit
shoulder surfing
skimming

16. Someone called Cecily to get her personal ID for her bank account. She may have been a victim of _____.

17. The _____ to whom Elizabeth owes money for her credit purchase is Macy's.

18. The _____ makes sure that your personal credit information only becomes available to firms legally allowed to access your information.

CHAPTER 9

Obtaining and Protecting Your Credit
CHECK YOUR KNOWLEDGE

Multiple Choice Questions *Circle the correct answer for each of the following.*

1. Which of the following is not one of the three main categories of credit?
   a. installment credit
   b. revolving open-end credit
   c. layaway credit
   d. noninstallment credit

2. Noninstallment credit is typically _____ in duration.
   a. 30 days or less
   b. more than six months
   c. one to four years
   d. two days

3. Installment loans typically require the borrower to make payments every _____.
   a. day
   b. week
   c. month
   d. year

4. Installment loans are usually used to buy all of the following except _____.
   a. furniture
   b. cars
   c. boats
   d. gas

5. Credit is advantageous because _____.
   a. it helps us make large purchases sooner than we could if using cash
   b. it is costly
   c. it makes financial matters more complex
   d. none of the above

6. Which of the following statements is not an example of the disadvantages of credit?
   a. Credit makes it easy to borrow too much money.
   b. Credit makes unwise purchases too easy.
   c. Using credit properly helps establish good credit history.
   d. Some credit carries extremely high interest rates.

7. Which of the following is not one of the three primary credit bureaus?
   a. Equifax
   b. Federal Credit Bureau
   c. TransUnion
   d. Experian

8. Credit reports contain all of the following except _____.
   a. records of late payment
   b. history of default
   c. medical records
   d. bankruptcy history

9. All of the following are common identity theft tactics except _____.
   a. shoulder surfing
   b. pretexting
   c. phishing
   d. sidewalk patrolling

10. Pretexting that occurs online is known as _____.
    a. skimming
    b. phishing
    c. shoulder surfing
    d. sidewalk patrolling

CHAPTER 9

Obtaining and Protecting Your Credit
MATH CHECK UP

Instructions: *In the space provided, answer each of the following math problems. Be sure to show your work in the space provided.*

1. Donielle opened a revolving line of credit with a $4,000 credit limit. How much does she still have available to borrow if she charged $1,100 but has paid back $200 of that amount?

2. Beth borrowed $1,500 from the bank at 8 percent interest and will make interest-only payments until the end of the year when she will pay off the entire amount. How much will her last payment for the entire amount be?

3. Corbin bought an audio system for his car that was $1,200. Assuming he pays the loan in full within six months, he will only be charged 6 percent annual interest. How much will his payment be if he waits until the last day to make a payment?

4. John charged $58.25, $111.58, and $12.29 on his credit card this month. How much will he owe if he pays the balance in full this month if his credit card charges 21 percent in annual interest?

5. Jason charged a $900 television at a local outlet store that offered free credit if the balance is paid in four months. If the balance is carried past that date, then an 18 percent annual interest rate is charged on the entire amount. If Jason waits until one day past the due date, how much interest will he be charged?

CHAPTER 9

Obtaining and Protecting Your Credit
OPEN RESPONSE #1: Making Purchases on Credit

Please answer all parts of the question in the space provided.

Prompt: Linney wants to buy furniture for his new apartment. He only needs living room furniture because his parents are letting him take the bedroom furniture from his room at home. The local furniture store is promoting "90 days, same as cash" for a living room set he really wants. They also are offering in-store credit (installment credit). Linney has the option of putting the purchase on his credit card. He wants to discuss with you what he should do.

1. Explain to Linney the advantages of the different types of credit for his purchase.

2. Explain to Linney the disadvantages of the different types of credit for his purchase.

Scoring Guide

4 Student gives correct answers for parts 1 and 2. All explanations are clear and complete. There is evidence of clear understanding of the concept.

3 Student gives correct answers for parts 1 and 2. Explanations are correct, but possibly unclear. There is less evidence of clear understanding.

2 Student answers 1 (1 or 2) part of the questions completely correct. There is some evidence of understanding.

1 Student gives only parts of correct answers. There is little evidence of understanding.

0 Response is totally incorrect or irrelevant (does not add any new information to the question).

CHAPTER 9

Obtaining and Protecting Your Credit
OPEN RESPONSE #2: Protecting Against Identity Theft

Please answer all parts of the question in the space provided.

Prompt: Andrea has heard on the news about the increase in identity theft. She would like to know more about how her identity could be stolen.

1. Explain to Andrea three ways criminals could steal her identity.

2. Explain three ways Andrea could protect herself against identity theft.

Scoring Guide

4 Student gives correct answers for parts 1 and 2. All explanations are clear and complete. There is evidence of clear understanding of the concept.

3 Student gives correct answers for parts 1 and 2. Explanations are correct, but possibly unclear. There is less evidence of clear understanding.

2 Student answers 1 (1 or 2) part of the questions completely correct. There is some evidence of understanding.

1 Student gives only parts of correct answers. There is little evidence of understanding.

0 Response is totally incorrect or irrelevant (does not add any new information to the question).

_____

_____

_____

_____

_____

_____

_____

_____

_____

_____

_____

_____

CHAPTER 9

Obtaining and Protecting Your Credit

ACTIVITY #1: Auto Financing

Instructions:

1. Research three sources of auto financing. Use online sources and local banks or financial institutions. Find the terms and rates offered for each financing source (remember to look at the differences for 12, 24, 36, or more months of financing).

2. Summarize your findings. Why are there differences in the terms and rates?

_____

_____

_____

_____

_____

_____

_____

_____

_____

_____

_____

_____

_____

_____

_____

_____

_____

_____

_____

_____

_____

_____

SCANS Foundation Skills: Basic and Thinking
SCANS Workplace Skills: Resources, Information, and Systems

CHAPTER 9

Obtaining and Protecting Your Credit

ACTIVITY #2: Addressing an Error in a Credit Report

Instructions:

1. Explain what to do if you find an error on your credit report. Provide the addresses of the three credit bureaus that are reporting information. You may find these online or through a local lending agency.

_____

_____

_____

_____

_____

_____

_____

_____

_____

_____

_____

_____

_____

_____

_____

_____

_____

_____

2. Use a separate sheet of paper, and write a letter you could send to each of the credit reporting agencies explaining that you have found an error on your credit report. The error is a loan to a local lending agency that you did not finance. It is someone else's loan whose name is fairly similar to yours. Request that the error be corrected.

SCANS Foundation Skills: Basic, Thinking, and Personal Qualities
SCANS Workplace Skills: Resources, Information, Systems, and Technology

CHAPTER 10

Personal Loans and Purchasing Decisions
VOCABULARY CHECK

1. Kayce found out she needed to take out a _____ to purchase her dirt bike.

2. When a mortgage has an interest rate that remains the same for the life of the loan, it is called a _____.

3. In order to help her get the dirt bike, Kayce's dad agreed to guarantee her loan by serving as a _____.

4. Brantley's mom inherited some jewelry worth about $25,000, so she decided to take out a _____ on their homeowners insurance to make sure it was adequately covered.

5. Kayce's loan would have an APR, or _____, of 8 percent.

6. Julie wanted to return to school, so she applied for a _____ because the financial aid office at the school said she was considered to have "exceptional" financial need.

7. Kayce's loan would be a _____ because the dirt bike would be pledged as _____ against loan repayment.

8. If Kayce was looking for a _____ without collateral, she would have an _____.

9. When a home is put up as collateral for a loan, this type of loan is called a _____.

10. Kayce found out she would need $500 for a _____ on her dirt bike to make sure she had some ownership in the bike before the bank would loan her money.

11. Keaton's parents have an _____ on their house.

12. The _____ for Kayce's loan would be at the end of 24 months.

13. Vannala's parents got a _____ at the bank to cover periodic shortfalls in cash flow for their new business.

14. Melody's parents got a _____ to make home improvements.

15. If Kayce _____ on the loan, she will lose the dirt bike and the money she has paid on the loan to date.

adjustable rate mortgage

annual percentage rate

collateral

cosigner

default

down payment

Federal Perkins loan

Federal Stafford loan

fixed-rate mortgage

home equity loan

lease

liability coverage

line of credit

maturity date

mortgage

personal loan

policy rider

secured loan

subprime mortgage

teaser rate

unsecured loan

16. Jessica wanted to purchase a car but looked into a _____ instead of buying.

17. Jordan did not qualify for a Federal Perkins loan, but based on his need he was able to get a _____ for his education.

18. The _____ on the loan was very low, but Marissa knew that she would pay much higher rates eventually.

19. Many people who got _____ defaulted on their loans and lost their homes.

20. Having _____ on his car helped protect Alphonse from financial disaster when he struck and injured a man with his car.

CHAPTER 10

Personal Loans and Purchasing Decisions
CHECK YOUR KNOWLEDGE

Multiple Choice Questions *Circle the correct answer for each of the following.*

1. Personal loans are typically used for large purchases such as _____.
   a. cars
   b. boats
   c. motorcycles
   d. all of the above

2. The fraction of an item's cost that a consumer pays up front is called the _____.
   a. down payment
   b. loan amount
   c. equity conversion
   d. liability

3. Personal loans usually mature in _____.
   a. two weeks
   b. 24 to 72 months
   c. 10 to 20 years
   d. none of the above

4. Sometimes a creditor may ask for a _____ to sign the loan documents. This person promises to repay the loan if the borrower defaults.
   a. cosigner
   b. lienor
   c. payee
   d. buyer

5. By law lenders are required to report the interest rate that factors in all of the relevant loan charges. This interest rate is known as the _____.
   a. teaser rate
   b. annual percentage rate
   c. loan rate
   d. prime rate

6. A(n) _____ loan has some asset pledged against it as collateral.
   a. unsecured
   b. covered
   c. teaser
   d. secured

7. Loans taken out to purchase a house are commonly called _____.
   a. subprimes
   b. teaser loans
   c. mortgages
   d. collateral

8. Loans that allow homeowners to borrow money using the equity in their homes as collateral are _____.
   a. adjustable rate loans
   b. mortgage teaser rates
   c. home equity loans
   d. illegal

9. Which of the following is not a reason to rent a home instead of buying one?
   a. if rent is cheaper
   b. if you intend to live in the area for only a few months
   c. if you are not familiar with the local real estate market
   d. if there are tax advantages to renting

10. Students with "exceptional" financial need may be eligible for subsidized loans known as _____, which carry very low interest rates and have longer grace periods than other subsidized student loans.
    a. Federal Stafford loans
    b. home equity loans
    c. Federal Perkins loans
    d. federal loans

CHAPTER 10

Personal Loans and Purchasing Decisions
MATH CHECK UP

Instructions: *In the space provided, answer each of the following math problems. Be sure to show your work in the space provided.*

1. If Naghia borrows $4,000 to buy a vehicle and her payment is $125.35 a month for 36 months, how much will she pay in interest over the life of the loan?

2. If Chu takes out an unsubsidized personal loan of $3,000 at 7 percent interest, which he does not have to begin repaying for 12 months, how much will the total amount of the loan be when he begins repayment?

3. Emilia lost $4,000 in personal belongings due to a flood at her apartment complex. Fortunately, she had renter's insurance with a $500 deductible. How much would she receive from the insurance company if her maximum coverage was $10,000?

4. Jamal wants to know how much he will be required to put down on a house that will cost $150,000 if the lender requires a 15 percent down payment.

5. Destiny needs to save a 20 percent down payment for a car she wants to buy. She knows cars of this make and year model tend to sell for about $6,000. How much will she need to save?

CHAPTER 10

Personal Loans and Purchasing Decisions
OPEN RESPONSE #1: Completing a Loan Application

Please answer all parts of the question in the space provided.

Prompt: Joshua is going to the bank to take out a personal loan. He has never done this before.

1. Explain to Joshua the three types of information that he will be asked to provide for the loan application.

2. Explain to Joshua the difference in a down payment and collateral for the loan.

Scoring Guide

4 Student gives correct answers for parts 1 and 2. All explanations are clear and complete. There is evidence of clear understanding of the concept.

3 Student gives correct answers for parts 1 and 2. Explanations are correct, but possibly unclear. There is less evidence of clear understanding.

2 Student answers 1 (1 or 2) part of the questions completely correct. There is some evidence of understanding.

1 Student gives only parts of correct answers. There is little evidence of understanding.

0 Response is totally incorrect or irrelevant (does not add any new information to the question).

_____

_____

_____

_____

_____

_____

_____

_____

_____

_____

_____

_____

_____

_____

CHAPTER 10

Personal Loans and Purchasing Decisions
OPEN RESPONSE #2: Buying versus Renting a Home

Please answer all parts of the question in the space provided.

Prompt: Shamika has just graduated from culinary school and has her first good paying job. She is very excited and is trying to decide about whether to buy or rent a home now that she is out on her own.

1. Explain to Shamika three questions she might ask herself in the decision making process and why each is important.

2. Explain to Shamika the importance of insurance, whether it is homeowners or renters, depending on her final decision to buy or rent a home.

Scoring Guide

4 Student gives correct answers for parts 1 and 2. All explanations are clear and complete. There is evidence of clear understanding of the concept.

3 Student gives correct answers for parts 1 and 2. Explanations are correct, but possibly unclear. There is less evidence of clear understanding.

2 Student answers 1 (1 or 2) part of the questions completely correct. There is some evidence of understanding.

1 Student gives only parts of correct answers. There is little evidence of understanding.

0 Response is totally incorrect or irrelevant (does not add any new information to the question).

_____

_____

_____

_____

_____

_____

_____

_____

_____

_____

_____

_____

_____

_____

_____

CHAPTER 10

Personal Loans and Purchasing Decisions

ACTIVITY #1: Calculating Down Payments and Amount Financed

Instructions:

1. Using the form provided, calculate the down payment and amount financed for the following personal loans for $4,500. Remember that the down payment will be subtracted from the loan amount.

Amount	Percentage of Loan Amount for Down Payment	Down Payment	Amount Financed
$4,500	2%		
$4,500	10%		
$4,500	8%		
$4,500	25%		

2. What are some possible reasons the interest rates vary so much? Write a summary of your reasoning. Be sure to provide evidence to support your conclusion. (Hint: these loans can be for different people.)

_____

_____

_____

_____

_____

_____

_____

_____

_____

_____

_____

CHAPTER 10

Personal Loans and Purchasing Decisions
ACTIVITY #2: Leasing versus Buying a Car

Instructions:

1. Using the following form, research the costs connected with the lease or purchase of two cars.

Car #1	Monthly Payment	Down Payment or Amount Due at Signing	Payment Due at End
Lease			
Purchase			
Car #2			
Lease			
Purchase			

2. Use this information to discuss the advantages and disadvantages of leasing or buying for each car. Be sure to use your research information to provide support for your findings. Defend your decision on which car you chose and why you purchased or leased it.

_____
_____
_____
_____
_____
_____
_____
_____
_____
_____

CHAPTER 11

Credit Cards and Other Forms of Credit
VOCABULARY CHECK

1. Justin received an application in the mail for a _____, but his parents advised him not to apply.

2. The _____ on Morgan's credit card is MyWay Bank.

3. The bank ran a _____ on Shawna before she received her loan.

4. Tina's credit card company offers _____ that allows her to exceed her credit limit—but at a hefty cost.

5. Tera is upset about the $39 _____ her credit card company charges every year.

6. Asa has a 20-day _____ to pay her credit card bill before it becomes past due.

7. Cord went to the ATM to get a _____ from his credit card to pay for movie night.

8. Melody wants to use _____ to combine her school loans and credit card debt in order to have a smaller payment.

9. _____ is the last resort to clear up debt and is reported to the credit bureau.

10. The money Rex received from _____ cost him $100 over what he borrowed for a two-week loan.

11. Jordan put his golf clubs up as collateral for a loan with the _____.

annual fee
bankruptcy
cash advance
credit card
credit check
credit provider
debt consolidation
grace period
overdraft protection
pawnbroker
payday lending

CHAPTER 11

Credit Cards and Other Forms of Credit

CHECK YOUR KNOWLEDGE

Multiple Choice Questions *Circle the correct answer for each of the following.*

1. Credit cards are _____.
   a. revolving open-end credit
   b. fixed term loan credit
   c. adjustable rate loan credit
   d. long-term credit

2. Which of the following is not an advantage of using credit cards?
   a. keeps you from having to carry cash or checks
   b. makes it easier to carry a low interest balance
   c. no interest charges accrue if balance is paid in full every cycle
   d. all of the above

3. Which of the following is a reason that merchants accept credit cards?
   a. decrease sales volume
   b. encourages more purchases
   c. saves the merchant money
   d. all of the above

4. A person's credit limit is _____.
   a. the maximum amount that may be borrowed
   b. irrelevant when making purchases
   c. unrelated to her credit history
   d. always below $1,000

5. Credit card grace periods are typically _____.
   a. 1 to 5 days
   b. 5 to 10 days
   c. six months
   d. 20 to 30 days

6. Credit card cash advances using an ATM are a(n) _____ source of funds.
   a. cheap
   b. costly
   c. cost neutral
   d. inaccessible

7. The process of combining several small loans into one larger loan that often carries a more favorable interest rate or maturity is known as _____.
   a. rollover
   b. debt consolidation
   c. payment branching
   d. combination cash

8. One new form of lending that provides low interest loans to most consumers is known as _____.
    a. pawnbroking
    b. payday lending
    c. tax refund lending
    d. none of the above

9. Pawn shops loan money in exchange for _____.
    a. your signature
    b. your paycheck
    c. holding some collateral, such as jewelry
    d. none of the above

10. Cell phone leases are typically for _____.
    a. one month
    b. two weeks or less
    c. five years
    d. one year

CHAPTER 11

Credit Cards and Other Forms of Credit
MATH CHECK UP

Instructions: *In the space provided, answer each of the following math problems. Be sure to show your work in the space provided.*

1. Jasmine's credit card has a $2,000 balance that she carried over from last month. Assuming her credit card charges an 18 percent annual interest rate, how much will her interest charges be this month?

2. Ramiro has accepted three credit card invitations and now has three cards with limits of $7,000, $5,000, and $9,500. He currently has these cards charged up to 75 percent of his limit. How much does he owe?

3. Gracie owes $4,200 on one credit card and $1,700 on another. The first card requires a minimum payment of 3 percent of the outstanding balance, and the second one requires a minimum payment of 4 percent of the outstanding balance. Assuming Gracie pays the minimum, how much will her payments total next month?

4. Kailin's grandfather just made a credit sale in his store of $1,243. Assuming the credit card company charges him a 2 percent fee, how much will he actually receive from this transaction?

5. Sandara's dad just got a cash advance from a payday lender. He wrote a check for $200 and received $170 in cash. The payday lender will hold the check for two weeks and then cash it. Approximately how much in annual interest is Sandara's dad paying for this cash advance?

CHAPTER 11

Credit Cards and Other Forms of Credit

OPEN RESPONSE #1: Types of Credit Cards and Various Features

Please answer all parts of the question in the space provided.

Prompt: Viola is trying to decide whether to apply for a credit card. She really would like to have one card but does not understand the different types and all the features.

1. Explain to Viola about the types of credit cards and the differences of each.

2. Explain to Viola three features the credit card companies might offer.

Scoring Guide

4 Student gives correct answers for parts 1 and 2. All explanations are clear and complete. There is evidence of clear understanding of the concept.

3 Student gives correct answers for parts 1 and 2. Explanations are correct, but possibly unclear. There is less evidence of clear understanding.

2 Student answers 1 (1 or 2) part of the questions completely correct. There is some evidence of understanding.

1 Student gives only parts of correct answers. There is little evidence of understanding.

0 Response is totally incorrect or irrelevant (does not add any new information to the question).

_____

_____

_____

_____

_____

_____

_____

_____

_____

_____

_____

_____

CHAPTER 11

Credit Cards and Other Forms of Credit
OPEN RESPONSE #2: Tips on Using Credit Cards

Please answer all parts of the question in the space provided.

Prompt: Sonny has just gotten his first credit card. He is very excited and shows it to you. Sonny suggests that both of you go on a shopping spree.

1. Explain to Sonny three tips on using his new credit card correctly.

2. Explain to Sonny the advantages and disadvantages of using his new credit card.

Scoring Guide

4 Student gives correct answers for parts 1 and 2. All explanations are clear and complete. There is evidence of clear understanding of the concept.

3 Student gives correct answers for parts 1 and 2. Explanations are correct, but possibly unclear. There is less evidence of clear understanding.

2 Student answers 1 (1 or 2) part of the questions completely correct. There is some evidence of understanding.

1 Student gives only parts of correct answers. There is little evidence of understanding.

0 Response is totally incorrect or irrelevant (does not add any new information to the question).

_____

_____

_____

_____

_____

_____

_____

_____

_____

_____

_____

_____

_____

_____

_____

_____

CHAPTER 11

Credit Cards and Other Forms of Credit
ACTIVITY #1: Credit Card Fees

Instructions:

1. Using the form provided, research three different credit cards (such as bank cards, store cards, American Express, and so forth) and the fees that are charged for using the cards. Use the Internet, interview parents or family members about their credit cards, or review applications that can be found at various locations.

Type of Card	Fees Charged

2. What fees are charged for each credit card company? Summarize your findings.

_____

_____

_____

_____

_____

_____

_____

_____

_____

_____

SCANS Foundation Skills: Basic and Thinking
SCANS Workplace Skills: Resources, Information, and Systems

CHAPTER 11

Credit Cards and Other Forms of Credit

ACTIVITY #2: Costly Credit Arrangements

Instructions:

1. Research information on payday lending, tax refund loans, and pawnbrokers. Gather information about agreement terms when you borrow from these lenders.

2. Use this information to write an informative paper that discusses the advantages and disadvantages of each of these credit arrangements. Be sure to use your research information to provide support for your findings.

CHAPTER 12

Banking Procedures and Services

VOCABULARY CHECK

1. Financial institutions that accept deposits and provide traditional checking and savings accounts are called _____.

2. Allstate Insurance is an example of a _____.

3. Natasha went to the _____ to get $40 in cash for the girls' afternoon of movie and lunch.

4. Tom opened a _____ so that he wouldn't have to carry as much cash, and he had his favorite football team emblem put on his _____.

5. Vera always writes in her _____ the amount she withdraws from the ATM.

6. Taundra wanted to earn interest on her checking account so she opened a _____.

7. Matt used his _____ to purchase gas for the trip but forgot to note it in his check register.

8. Jonas's parents keep a copy of their will in a _____ at the bank.

9. The used car dealer required Holly to pay by _____ if she wanted to take the car immediately without waiting for her personal check to clear the bank.

10. Jeff used a _____ from the U.S. Post Office to pay for the Xbox he purchased on eBay.

11. Band members were told to carry _____ for their European trip.

12. Sasha set up her car payments on _____ to be paid automatically. This is an example of _____.

13. The _____ insures depositors' money in banks while _____ insures depositors' money in credit unions.

14. Jordan belonged to a _____, which offered a higher interest rate for his savings account than other local banks.

15. The formal name for the central bank of the United States is the _____.

automatic teller machine (ATM)

bank draft

cashier's check

check

check register

checking account

credit union

debit card

depository institutions

discount rate

electronic funds transfer

Federal Deposit Insurance Corporation (FDIC)

Federal Reserve System

fiat money

inflation

monetary policy

money orders

National Credit Union Share Insurance Fund (NCUSIF)

negotiable order of withdrawal (NOW) accounts

nondepository institutions

personal identification number (PIN)

16. _____ is one of the main goals of Fed policy.

17. When the overall level of prices is increasing it is known as _____.

18. The primary tool to fight inflation and promote a healthy economy is _____.

19. A dollar bill and quarters are examples of _____.

20. Occasionally the Fed will change the interest rate it charges to banks when it loans them money. This interest rate is known as the _____.

21. It's not a good idea to keep your _____ in your wallet.

price level stability

safety deposit boxes

travelers checks

130

CHAPTER 12

Banking Procedures and Services

CHECK YOUR KNOWLEDGE

Multiple Choice Questions *Circle the correct answer for each of the following.*

1. Depository institutions include all of the following except _____.
   a. banks
   b. credit unions
   c. life insurance companies
   d. savings banks

2. A _____ is a written order instructing your bank to pay money from your account to another party.
   a. check
   b. ATM
   c. debit card
   d. cash withdrawal

3. The U.S. Postal Service issues _____ that function similar to cashier's checks.
   a. checks
   b. money orders
   c. travelers checks
   d. CDs

4. Nondepository institutions include _____.
   a. banks
   b. life insurance companies
   c. credit unions
   d. savings banks

5. Banks provide a number of services including all of the following except _____.
   a. payday lending
   b. safety deposit boxes
   c. checking accounts
   d. cashier's checks

6. Banks have insurance on deposits through the _____.
   a. National Credit Union Share Insurance Fund
   b. Federal Deposit Insurance Corporation
   c. State Depositor Reconciliation Fund
   d. Securities Insurance Fund

7. The central bank of the United States is called the _____.
   a. National U.S. Bank
   b. Federal Reserve
   c. Central Banking Authority
   d. Monetary Bank of the United States

8. Money that has value because the government says it does is _____.
   a. gold
   b. silver
   c. state
   d. fiat money

9. The Federal Reserve uses _____ to fight inflation and promote economic growth.
   a. monetary policy
   b. fiscal policy
   c. legislation
   d. legal action

10. In order to reduce interest rates the Fed will _____ the money supply.
   a. increase
   b. decrease
   c. stabilize
   d. maintain

CHAPTER 12

Banking Procedures and Services

MATH CHECK UP

Instructions: *In the space provided, answer each of the following math problems. Be sure to show your work in the space provided.*

1. Ramesh has $272,000 in a CD at a local bank. If the bank goes out of business what is the maximum amount he could lose?

2. Jucinda has $423 in her checking account according to the bank. However, she has written checks for $21.24 and $38.12 that have not cleared the bank. How much does she have available in her checking account to spend?

3. Nathan's statement indicated his NOW account had earned $1.21 in interest and that he had been charged $12 for the purchase of some checks. He also went to the ATM machine this morning to take out $80 after having received his statement in the mail. If Nathan's register says he has $544 in his account, what does he really have available to spend?

4. Nai deposited two checks for $235 and $300 in her checking account. Assuming her original balance was $578.34 and she has one check outstanding that has not cleared the bank yet for $411.98, how much is her balance?

5. Brandon wrote a check for $28.29 for a pair of shoes that caused him to overdraw at the bank. Assuming the bank charged him $25 for the "bounced" check and the merchant charged him $30, how much did he pay in total for the shoes?

CHAPTER 12

Banking Procedures and Services

OPEN RESPONSE #1: Writing a Check

Please answer all parts of the question in the space provided.

Prompt: Sasha has his first checking account. He has never written a check but needs to make a car payment.

1. Explain to Sasha the five parts of a check.

2. Explain to Sasha how to fill out his check and then post the amount in the check register.

Scoring Guide

4 Student gives correct answers for parts 1 and 2. All explanations are clear and complete. There is evidence of clear understanding of the concept.

3 Student gives correct answers for parts 1 and 2. Explanations are correct, but possibly unclear. There is less evidence of clear understanding.

2 Student answers 1 (1 or 2) part of the questions completely correct. There is some evidence of understanding.

1 Student gives only parts of correct answers. There is little evidence of understanding.

0 Response is totally incorrect or irrelevant (does not add any new information to the question).

CHAPTER 12

Banking Procedures and Services

OPEN RESPONSE #2: Types of Banking Services

Please answer all parts of the question in the space provided.

Prompt: Cyril's little sister wants to learn about banks and banking services. She has asked him to take her to the bank so she can learn more. Cyril takes her to the customer service representative at his bank.

1. As the customer service representative, explain to Cyril's sister three services that are offered at the bank.

2. Explain how her money would be protected once it has been deposited in the bank.

Scoring Guide

4 Student gives correct answers for parts 1 and 2. All explanations are clear and complete. There is evidence of clear understanding of the concept.

3 Student gives correct answers for parts 1 and 2. Explanations are correct, but possibly unclear. There is less evidence of clear understanding.

2 Student answers 1 (1 or 2) part of the questions completely correct. There is some evidence of understanding.

1 Student gives only parts of correct answers. There is little evidence of understanding.

0 Response is totally incorrect or irrelevant (does not add any new information to the question).

CHAPTER 12

Banking Procedures and Services

ACTIVITY #1: Writing a Check

Using the following information, complete the blank check below.

Payee: Johnson Game Stop Store
Amount: $27.95
Date: (use current date)
Payer: (use your name)
For: Xbox game

101

_____

123 Main Street
Your Town, USA 12345-6789   Date: _____

Pay to the
order of: _____ $ [   ]

_____ DOLLARS

_____

Memo _____   _____

12345678* 0101

CHAPTER 12

Banking Procedures and Services

ACTIVITY #2: Check Register

Instructions:

1. Using the transactions below, post each transaction to the check register.

   a. June 2, Deposit of $250.00
   b. June 2, ATM withdrawal, $40.00
   c. June 14, Check #1234, $62.85, local electric company
   d. June 14, Check #1235, $114.95, cell phone bill
   e. June 21, ATM withdrawal, $20.00
   f. June 23, Check 1236, $50.00, high school cheerleaders
   g. June 29, Check 1237, $12.20, gas
   h. June 30, Deposit of $125.00
   i. June 30, electronic transfer, $369.00, car payment

CHECK NUMBER	DATE	DESCRIPTION OF TRANSACTION	PAYMENT/DEBIT (-)	✔	FEE (-)	DEPOSIT/CREDIT (+)	BALANCE $	

2. Complete the information about the check register in the blanks provided.

   Beginning balance: $1,080.00

   Withdrawal total: _____

   Deposits: _____

   Ending balance: _____

SCANS Foundation Skills: Basic and Thinking

SCANS Workplace Skills: Resources, Information, and Systems

CHAPTER 12

Banking Procedures and Services

ACTIVITY #3: Bank Reconciliation

Instructions:

Using the following bank statement and the check register from Activity #2, complete the bank statement reconciliation.

Your Bank		
ANYTOWN, STATE 00000-0000		
CUSTOMER SERVICE 24 HOURS A DAY, 000-000-0000		ACCOUNT
YOUR NAME		XXXXX
123 MAIN STREET		STATEMENT PERIOD
YOUR TOWN, STATE 12345-6789		6-1-2013 – 6-30-2013
THANK YOU FOR BANKING WITH US		
SUMMARY OF YOUR ACCOUNTS		
CHECKING		SAVINGS
BEGINNING BALANCE	1080.00	
DEPOSITS	375.00	
WITHDRAWALS	669.00	
SERVICE CHARGES/FEES	0.00	
ENDING BALANCE	786.00	
CHECKING ACTIVITY		
DEPOSITS		
POSTED	AMOUNT	DESCRIPTION
6-02	250.00	DEPOSIT
6-30	125.00	DEPOSIT
WITHDRAWALS		
CHECK NO.	PAID	AMOUNT
1234	6-18	62.85
1235	6-19	114.95
1236	6-25	50.00
1237	6-29	12.20
POSTED	AMOUNT	DESCRIPTION
6-02	40.00	ATM WITHDRAWAL
6-21	20.00	ATM WITHDRAWAL
6-30	369.00	CAR PAYMENT
CHECKING SERVICES CHARGE AND FEE SUMMARY		
AMOUNT	DESCRIPTION	
0.00	MONTHLY SERVICE CHARGE	

CHAPTER 13

Methods of Saving
VOCABULARY CHECK

1. How quickly you can turn an asset into cash without a significant loss refers to _____.

2. When Levi put money into his checking account, it was considered a _____ because it can be withdrawn at any time.

3. Kristin did not need check writing capability and she also wanted to receive a higher interest on her money than a NOW account might pay, so she opened a _____.

4. Paddy got a 12-month _____ with his graduation money so that it would earn a higher interest rate than if he had put it into a savings account. He knew he would not need access to his money for at least a year.

5. Katie wanted to earn a high interest rate but wanted to be able to withdraw money when needed, so she opened a _____, which allows her to write five checks a month without penalty.

6. Jaana looked at the _____ on two different CD options before deciding which would be best for her to invest in.

7. The government created _____ named after sections in the IRS code to encourage people to save for retirement.

8. Nyles opened a _____ for his retirement money because he could make _____ and the earnings would be _____.

9. Although it has its own unique features, a _____ has the same contributions limits as the traditional IRA but the money is not taxed at withdrawal.

10. Camelia was amazed at how much she could accumulate for retirement simply by putting money into accounts where she could take advantage of _____.

11. If you are self-employed, you may be eligible to participate in a type of IRA called a _____.

401(k)/403(b) plans

annual percentage yield (APY)

annuity

certificate of deposit (CD)

compound interest

defined-benefit plan

defined-contribution plan

demand deposit

employer-sponsored retirement plan

fixed annuity

individual retirement account (IRA)

liquidity

money market deposit account (MMDA)

pension plan

roth IRA

savings account

SEP-IRA

tax deductible

tax deferred

traditional IRA

variable annuity

vesting

12. Li accepted a job because they offered a _____, which would guarantee him a specific amount of income when he retired. These types of plans are also commonly known as _____, and they are a type of _____.

13. The process of working a certain length of time to become eligible for certain benefits is known as _____.

14. Li interviewed for a job that offered a _____ in which the employer would contribute to his retirement but it gave no guarantee of specific retirement benefits.

15. A type of savings account created by the government to encourage people to save for retirement is known as an _____.

16. A financial product that guarantees annual payment to the owner for a fixed period of time or a lifetime is called a(n) _____.

17. An annuity whose return and ultimate payment is a guaranteed amount is called a _____.

18. An annuity whose return and payment depends on the performance of investments is called a _____.

CHAPTER 13

Methods of Saving

CHECK YOUR KNOWLEDGE

Multiple Choice Questions *Circle the correct answer for each of the following.*

1. Bank accounts that offer more liquidity to the depositor pay a _____ rate of interest.
   a. higher
   b. lower
   c. stable
   d. very high

2. A demand deposit account that functions as an interest-bearing checking account is called a _____.
   a. time shared account
   b. checking account
   c. negotiable order of withdrawal account
   d. shared repurchase interest account

3. Interest bearing savings accounts are commonly called _____ accounts.
   a. checking
   b. withdrawal
   c. seasonal savings
   d. passbook savings

4. Certificates of deposits (CDs) have _____ maturity dates.
   a. six month
   b. specified
   c. uncertain
   d. five year

5. Traditional individual retirement accounts are _____.
   a. taxed at withdrawal
   b. taxed at deferment
   c. taxed at time of deposit
   d. never taxed

6. Retirement plans that guarantee a specific amount of income at retirement are known as _____.
   a. defined contribution plans
   b. defined benefit plans
   c. guaranteed income plans
   d. IRAs

7. Nonprofit organizations can set up defined contribution retirement plans that are referred to as_____.
   a. 401k plans
   b. IRAs
   c. vesting plans
   d. 403b plans

8. The process of earning eligibility in a retirement plan is called _____.
   a. earning
   b. vesting
   c. selling
   d. working

9. The popular name for defined-benefit retirement plans is _____.
   a. pension
   b. IRA
   c. CD
   d. defined-contribution

10. Credit unions differ from banking institutions in that they have _____ status.
   a. for profit
   b. legal
   c. nonprofit
   d. education

CHAPTER 13

Methods of Saving
MATH CHECK UP

Instructions: *In the space provided, answer each of the following math problems. Be sure to show your work in the space provided.*

1. Jamal bought a $5,000 CD that pays 3.5 percent interest and matures in two years. During the second year he will earn interest on the principal and the first year's interest. How much interest will he earn in year two?

2. Refer to the previous problem. How much will Jamal's CD be worth at maturity?

3. Brianne put $4,000 in her passbook savings account that earns 2 percent annually. She also bought an $8,000 one-year CD that pays 3.8 percent annually. How much will she earn in interest during the year?

4. Shanique put $3,200 in a three-year CD that pays 4 percent a year. How much will it be worth at maturity?

5. Lakinta's employer matches her 401k contributions with a 50 percent match up to $5,000 a year. Assuming she put $7,000 in her 401k, how much were the total contributions to this account for the year?

CHAPTER 13

Methods of Saving

OPEN RESPONSE #1: Types of Bank Accounts

Please answer all parts of the question in the space provided.

Prompt: Ian has his first job. He wants to open a bank account and has asked you to explain his options.

1. Explain to Ian three different types of accounts available to him.

2. Explain the advantages and disadvantages of each type of account.

Scoring Guide

4 Student gives correct answers for parts 1 and 2. All explanations are clear and complete. There is evidence of clear understanding of the concept.

3 Student gives correct answers for parts 1 and 2. Explanations are correct, but possibly unclear. There is less evidence of clear understanding.

2 Student answers 1 (1 or 2) part of the questions completely correct. There is some evidence of understanding.

1 Student gives only parts of correct answers. There is little evidence of understanding.

0 Response is totally incorrect or irrelevant (does not add any new information to the question).

CHAPTER 13

Methods of Saving

OPEN RESPONSE #2: Types of Retirement Savings

Please answer all parts of the question in the space provided.

Prompt: Kylie is about to graduate and is job searching. She knows about looking at salary, opportunities to advance, and benefits offered. Kylie is interested in saving for retirement but wants to know about doing it individually versus looking at employer-sponsored retirement.

1. Explain to Kylie two types of individual retirement accounts.

2. Explain to Kylie about two forms of employer-sponsored retirement accounts.

Scoring Guide

4 Student gives correct answers for parts 1 and 2. All explanations are clear and complete. There is evidence of clear understanding of the concept.

3 Student gives correct answers for parts 1 and 2. Explanations are correct, but possibly unclear. There is less evidence of clear understanding.

2 Student answers 1 (1 or 2) part of the questions completely correct. There is some evidence of understanding.

1 Student gives only parts of correct answers. There is little evidence of understanding.

0 Response is totally incorrect or irrelevant (does not add any new information to the question).

CHAPTER 13

Methods of Saving

ACTIVITY #1: Comparing Financial Institutions

Instructions:

1. Use the following form to research current interest rates offered by two different financial institutions on the types of financial products or accounts they offer, which might include savings accounts, NOW accounts, and CDs.

Current Interest Rates

Name of Financial Institution	Savings Account	NOW Account	CD	Other

2. Write a summary of your findings.

_____
_____
_____
_____
_____
_____
_____
_____
_____
_____
_____
_____
_____
_____
_____
_____

SCANS Foundation Skills: Basic and Thinking

SCANS Workplace Skills: Resources, Information, and Systems

CHAPTER 13

Methods of Saving

ACTIVITY #2: Retirement Savings

Instructions:

1. Use the Internet to find a traditional/Roth IRA calculator. A link to one such calculator is provided in this chapter.

2. Use the following form to calculate savings at retirement if you invest $2,000 per year.

Retirement Savings at Age 65

Years of Investing	Annual Rate of Return	Amount in Traditional IRA	Amount in Roth IRA
20 years	8 percent		
30 years	8 percent		
40 years	8 percent		

3. Write a summary of your findings. In your summary, explain the advantage of saving early for retirement and the difference between the traditional IRA and the Roth IRA at retirement.

_____

_____

_____

_____

_____

_____

_____

_____

_____

_____

_____

_____

_____

SCANS Foundation Skills: Basic and Thinking

SCANS Workplace Skills: Resources, Information, and Systems

CHAPTER 14

Methods of Investing

VOCABULARY CHECK

1. Emilio's _____ portfolio has stocks, bonds, mutual funds and real estate.

2. Krisztina has purchased _____ in a company, which represents a piece of ownership.

3. When a company "goes public," this first sale of stock is called a(n) _____.

4. The _____ is where the initial public offering occurs.

5. When stock sales are reported in the newspapers or in the financial news, these transactions occurred in the

   _____.

6. A stock is _____ when the company is trading on a stock exchange such as the NYSE or NASDAQ.

7. The secondary market includes the _____

   _____.

8. A large pension fund is an example of an

   _____.

9. Myles likes to evaluate companies and pick his own stocks. He is considered an _____.

10. Companies sometimes pay cash distributions known as _____ to the companies' owners who are known as _____.

11. The government agency that regulates and monitors the stock market is called the _____.

12. A stock and/or bond issued by governments and businesses is commonly referred to as a _____.

13. Merrill Lynch is an example of a _____ firm because its brokers advise and execute trades.

14. When you trade on E*TRADE or similar companies, you are working with a _____, who offers lower _____ but a reduced level of service.

15. A _____ is a promissory note, or a promise to repay a certain amount of money at a future date.

16. The expiration date of a bond is called the _____.

bond
brokerage
commission
corporate bond
coupon payment
coupon rate
discount brokerage
diversification
dividend
face value
federal agency bonds
full-service brokerage
initial public offering (IPO)
institutional investor
investment
junk bond
maturity date
municipal bond
mutual fund
National Association of Securities Dealers Automatic Quotation (NASDAQ) System
New York Stock Exchange (NYSE)
primary market
publicly traded
secondary market
Securities and Exchange Commission (SEC)

17. The maturity value of a bond is shown on the front of the bond, known as _____.

18. A bond's interest rate, or _____, represents the interest due on the bond. The regular interest payments are also called _____.

19. The debt of the United States government is financed with _____.

20. FHA or Ginnie Mae may issue bonds known as _____.

21. To finance large public projects such as water or sewer systems, state or local government may issue _____.

22. _____ are issued by large firms and have all degrees of risk. Those with the highest risk are called _____.

23. _____ will typically own a wide range of investments. Multiple investments in a variety of different types of investments are called _____.

24. The _____ is an example of a secondary market that uses an auction system to trade stocks.

25. A _____ firm executes investment trades for investors.

security

shareholder

stock

Treasury bonds

CHAPTER 14

Methods of Investing

CHECK YOUR KNOWLEDGE

Multiple Choice Questions *Circle the correct answer for each of the following.*

1. Liquid investments include all of the following except _____.
   a. stocks
   b. certificates of deposit
   c. savings accounts
   d. checking accounts

2. The biggest problem with liquid investments is that they_____.
   a. generate high returns
   b. create significant tax liabilities
   c. earn low returns
   d. are difficult to redeem

3. When a company "goes public," the first sale of stock is called _____.
   a. an IPO
   b. a CD
   c. the NYSE
   d. the NASDAQ

4. The most famous stock exchange where stocks are traded using an auction system is _____.
   a. E*TRADE
   b. Cybor
   c. IPO
   d. the NYSE

5. A fractional ownership in a company is called a _____.
   a. stock
   b. CD
   c. bond
   d. dividend

6. Brokerage firms typically charge a fee known as a_____ for carrying out transactions.
   a. sale price
   b. initial public offering
   c. commission
   d. security

7. All of the following are types of bonds except _____.
   a. municipal
   b. Treasury
   c. corporate
   d. executive

8. Treasury bonds are issued by the United States government to finance our _____.
   a. national debt
   b. taxes
   c. banking system
   d. Social Security system

9. Mutual funds are attractive for all of the following reasons except _____.
   a. professional management
   b. high risk
   c. diversification benefits
   d. low initial investment

10. Which of the following is not a method of investing in real estate?
   a. owning your own home
   b. buying rental property
   c. owning timberland
   d. buying a bond mutual fund

CHAPTER 14

Methods of Investing

MATH CHECK UP

Instructions: *In the space provided, answer each of the following math problems. Be sure to show your work in the space provided.*

1. Nathaniel bought 60 shares of General Electric stock for $29.25 a share. He sold it one year later for $38.50 a share. What was Nathaniel's dollar return?

2. Jillian purchased a $1,000 face value bond that carried an 8 percent coupon rate. How much did she receive in interest if she held the bond for two years?

3. Raul bought 45 shares of stock for $36 a share. He sold it one year later for $38 a share. What was his percentage return?

4. In the previous problem, how much would Raul's percentage return be if he received a $1 dividend during that year?

5. What is the total value of your stock portfolio if you own 25 shares of GE stock valued at $31 a share and 120 shares of Wal-Mart stock valued at $42 a share?

CHAPTER 14

Methods of Investing

OPEN RESPONSE #1: Investing in Stocks

Please answer all parts of the question in the space provided.

Prompt: Zach has an extra job working at home using his computer. He has saved $10,000 in a savings account. Zach wants to have his money grow long-term.

1. Explain to Zach why investing some or all of the $10,000 in stocks or bonds might be a good idea.

2. Explain to Zach the difference between a full-service broker and a discount broker.

Scoring Guide

4 Student gives correct answers for parts 1 and 2. All explanations are clear and complete. There is evidence of clear understanding of the concept.

3 Student gives correct answers for parts 1 and 2. Explanations are correct, but possibly unclear. There is less evidence of clear understanding.

2 Student answers 1 (1 or 2) part of the questions completely correct. There is some evidence of understanding.

1 Student gives only parts of correct answers. There is little evidence of understanding.

0 Response is totally incorrect or irrelevant (does not add any new information to the question).

CHAPTER 14

Methods of Investing

OPEN RESPONSE #2: Investing in Bonds

Please answer all parts of the question in the space provided.

Prompt: Keasha is thinking about investing in bonds. She is unsure how bonds work.

1. Explain to Keasha how bonds work.

2. Explain to Keasha three types of bonds available to her.

Scoring Guide

4 Student gives correct answers for parts 1 and 2. All explanations are clear and complete. There is evidence of clear understanding of the concept.

3 Student gives correct answers for parts 1 and 2. Explanations are correct, but possibly unclear. There is less evidence of clear understanding.

2 Student answers 1 (1 or 2) part of the questions completely correct. There is some evidence of understanding.

1 Student gives only parts of correct answers. There is little evidence of understanding.

0 Response is totally incorrect or irrelevant (does not add any new information to the question).

CHAPTER 14

Methods of Investing

ACTIVITY #1: New York Stock Exchange (NYSE)

1. Use the form below and follow one stock on the NYSE for one week. You may use the Internet, newspaper, or local stock broker to help you gather information on your stock.

2. Write a summary paper explaining how the stock performed during the week.

3. Complete the following table:

NYSE Symbol for Your Stock:
_____

Closing Price Each Day				
Day 1	Day 2	Day 3	Day 4	Day 5

CHAPTER 14

Methods of Investing
ACTIVITY #2: Risk Tolerance

Instructions:

1. Turn to page 272 of Chapter 14. Take the Risk Tolerance Quiz.

2. Report your results here: _____

3. Discuss your results. Were there any questions you could have answered either way? Which one(s)? Why? Did the results turn out how you thought they would? Explain.

_____

_____

_____

_____

_____

_____

_____

_____

_____

_____

_____

_____

_____

_____

_____

_____

_____

_____

_____

_____

_____

_____

CHAPTER 14

Methods of Investing

ACTIVITY #3: Investigating Bonds

Instructions:

1. Use the newspaper or Internet to research three different bonds available. Gather information identifying the following:

   type
   maturity date
   coupon rate
   purpose
   rating

2. Develop a chart showing the information gathered about each bond.

3. Write a summation of your findings.

_____
_____
_____
_____
_____
_____
_____
_____
_____
_____
_____
_____
_____
_____
_____
_____
_____
_____
_____
_____

CHAPTER 15

Planning for the Future
VOCABULARY CHECK

1. Investing your money with the knowledge that longer time horizons will help you accumulate larger amounts is applying the principle of the _____.

2. The projected value of a sum of money at some point in the future is called the _____.

3. Earning interest on principal and interest is the process of _____.

4. The value of a sum of money at the present time is called _____.

5. When interest is earned only on the original amount or principle this is called _____.

6. When you want to calculate how long it will take to double your money for a given interest rate, you can use the _____ to help you make an approximation.

7. Alessia's investment _____ consists of real estate, stocks, and bonds.

8. Jacob did not want to invest only in one stock or bond. He actually spread his money among different investments to reduce his risk, which is called _____.

9. Different types of investments with different levels of risk are called _____.

10. The process of spreading your investments among assets classes is called _____.

11. As part of their _____ process, Rhaj's parents determined how their wealth would be distributed on or before their deaths.

12. Lynden was a minor so his parents had a _____ that stated who would be his legal guardian if something happened to both of them.

13. Lynden's parents stated that he would be one _____ in their will.

14. If someone dies without a will, he or she is said to be _____.

15. Estate planning often includes establishing a _____ to transfer assets in a manner that avoids taxes.

asset allocation

asset classes

beneficiary

compounding

diversification

estate planning

future value

intestate

portfolio

present value

rule of 72

simple interest

time value of money

trust

will

CHAPTER 15

Planning for the Future

CHECK YOUR KNOWLEDGE

Multiple Choice Questions *Circle the correct answer for each of the following.*

1. The time value of money refers to the fact that _____.
   a. time is costly
   b. watches are very expensive
   c. money received today has more value than money received next year
   d. none of the above

2. Present value refers to the _____.
   a. value of a sum of money now
   b. value of a gift received
   c. value of a sum of money in the future
   d. value of investments at retirement

3. The process of earning interest on interest already received is called _____.
   a. simple interest
   b. compounding
   c. facilitating
   d. present valuing

4. The rule of 72 tells us that your money will double in _____ years if you are earning a 12 percent return.
   a. 4
   b. 8
   c. 72
   d. 6

5. The process of spreading your investments across several different types of asset classes is called _____.
   a. portfolios
   b. asset allocation
   c. risk assumption
   d. investment smoothing

6. You will find that investments that offer higher rates of return also require you to accept a higher level of _____.
   a. cash
   b. diversification
   c. risk
   d. CDs

7. The process of determining how your wealth will be distributed at your death is
   _____.
   a. estate planning
   b. asset allocation
   c. diversification
   d. estate taxation

8. A(n) _____ is a legal request of how your wealth will be distributed when you die.
   a. estate
   b. will
   c. tax
   d. certificate

9. Assuming a constant rate of return on your investments, you would accumulate the most wealth if you began investing at age _____.
   a. 15
   b. 20
   c. 35
   d. 50

10. Interest earned only on the original principal amount is called _____ interest.
    a. compound
    b. savings
    c. simple
    d. mortgage

CHAPTER 15

Planning for the Future
MATH CHECK UP

Instructions: *In the space provided, answer each of the following math problems. Be sure to show your work in the space provided.*

1. How much is $4,000 that you will receive in one year worth today if you could earn 7 percent on the money?

2. How much interest will you earn the fourth year on a $2,000 deposit that pays simple interest of 6 percent?

3. How much interest would you earn in the fourth year on a $2,000 deposit that earns 6 percent that was compounded annually?

4. If you invested $5,000 for 20 years and could earn 10 percent a year, how much money would you accumulate?

5. Gerard bought some land for $45,000 that he thinks will grow 15 percent a year in value for five years. How much will it be worth in five years?

CHAPTER 15

Planning for the Future

OPEN RESPONSE #1: Time Value of Money

Please answer all parts of the question in the space provided.

Prompt: Loralie is trying to understand how people become millionaires by saving money. She would really like to have more than $1 million when she is age 65 but she is not sure how that can happen.

1. Explain to Loralie the concept of the time value of money. Provide her with an example to help her understand this tool.

2. Explain to Loralie what is meant by "your money begins to work for you instead of you working for your money."

Scoring Guide

4 Student gives correct answers for parts 1 and 2. All explanations are clear and complete. There is evidence of clear understanding of the concept.

3 Student gives correct answers for parts 1 and 2. Explanations are correct, but possibly unclear. There is less evidence of clear understanding.

2 Student answers 1 (1 or 2) part of the questions completely correct. There is some evidence of understanding.

1 Student gives only parts of correct answers. There is little evidence of understanding.

0 Response is totally incorrect or irrelevant (does not add any new information to the question).

_____

_____

_____

_____

_____

_____

_____

_____

_____

_____

_____

_____

CHAPTER 15

Planning for the Future

OPEN RESPONSE #2: Investment Portfolio

Please answer all parts of the question in the space provided.

Prompt: Lars has investments that were made for him when he was young. Now, at age 18 he has been advised it is time to begin managing his portfolio himself.

1. Explain to Lars what his portfolio represents and why it is important to review his portfolio regularly.

2. Explain to Lars what diversification is and why it is important to his financial future.

Scoring Guide

4 Student gives correct answers for parts 1 and 2. All explanations are clear and complete. There is evidence of clear understanding of the concept.

3 Student gives correct answers for parts 1 and 2. Explanations are correct, but possibly unclear. There is less evidence of clear understanding.

2 Student answers 1 (1 or 2) part of the questions completely correct. There is some evidence of understanding.

1 Student gives only parts of correct answers. There is little evidence of understanding.

0 Response is totally incorrect or irrelevant (does not add any new information to the question).

CHAPTER 15

Planning for the Future

ACTIVITY #1: Future Value

Instructions:

1. Use the form below to post calculations of future value of investments. Use a financial calculator. You can find several of these on the Internet.

Future Value

Amount Invested Annually

Years	$2,000	$3,000	$4,000
20			
30			
40			

2. Summarize how a change in years or the amount invested can change the future value.

_____

_____

_____

_____

_____

_____

_____

_____

_____

_____

_____

_____

_____

_____

_____

CHAPTER 15

Planning for the Future
ACTIVITY #2: Risk and Return Trade-Off

Instructions:

1. Consider three possible investments: purchasing CDs, buying stock in a large, established company, and investing in an emu farm owned by your neighbor. Where possible, research the possible rates of return and history of performance for each investment opportunity. Consider the risks involved in each. Develop a chart to show the information for each investment.

2. Summarize your results. What are the differences in each investment? What are the advantages and disadvantages of each investment? Which investment would you be willing to invest in, and why?

_____

_____

_____

_____

_____

_____

_____

_____

_____

_____

_____

_____

_____

_____

_____

_____

_____

_____

_____

_____

_____

SCANS Foundation Skills: Basic and Thinking
SCANS Workplace Skills: Resources, Information, and Systems